CROSS-BORDER LINKS

CROSS-BORDER LINKS

A Directory of Organizations in Canada, Mexico, and the United States

Edited by Ricardo Hernández & Edith Sánchez

Inter-Hemispheric Education Resource Center / Albuquerque, New Mexico

First Edition, September 1992
Second Printing, July 1993

Co-produced with Action Canada Network

and Equipo Pueblo

PUEBLO

ORGANIZACION NO GUBERNAMENTAL DE DESARROLLO

Production and design by John Hawley / Resource Center

Published by the Inter-Hemispheric Education Resource Center

Inter-Hemispheric Education Resource Center
Box 4506 / Albuquerque, New Mexico 87196

Library of Congress Cataloging-in-Publication Data

Cross-border links : a directory of organizations in Canada, Mexico, and the United States / edited by Ricardo Hernandez & Edith Sanchez—1st ed.

p. cm.

Includes index.

ISBN 0-911213-38-4 (pbk. : $14.95)

1. Associations, institutions, etc.—United States—Directories. 2. Associations, institutions, etc.—Canada—Directories. 3. Associations, institutions, etc.—Mexico—Directories. 4. North America—Economic integration. I. Hernandez, Ricardo, 1955- II. Sanchez, Edith, 1972-
HS61. A2C76 1992
061—dc20 92-71799

ACKNOWLEDGMENTS

This directory was made possible through the contributions of a number of friendly people. Our thanks go first of all to Harry Browne, who supplemented his research and analysis for many parts of the book with daily feedback and assistance. Special thanks go also to Beth Sims for her work on the government and academic sections, and to Tom Barry who conceptualized the general framework of the directory. A pillar of support both personally and in coordinating production of the entire effort was Debra Preusch. Since Spanish is our first language, we owe special thanks to Chuck Hosking, who patiently edited the manuscript. The design and production of the book was managed by John Hawley. Rose Hansen, Miguel Margarida, and Jodi Gibson assisted with research.

We are especially grateful for their fountain of contacts and for helpful comments on sections of the manuscript to: Mary McGinn, David Brooks, Matt Witt, Primitivo Rodríguez, Pharis Harvey, Geoffrey Bogart, Geoffrey Land, Gray Newman, David Ranney, Mary Kelly, Dick Kamp, Jonathan Fox, and George Baker in the United States; Carlos Heredia, Rosy Caudillo, Elaine Burns, Silvia Sandoval, SIPRO, and the Canadian Embassy in Mexico; Randy Robinson, Bruce Campbell, Ken Traynor, Juanita Montalvo, Ann Weston, and Lisa Shaw in Canada.

The Cross-Border Links project would not have been possible without generous support from Frontier Internship in Mission, the W.K. Kellogg Foundation, the John D. and Catherine T. MacArthur Foundation, and the Presbyterian Hunger Program.

Thanks, as well, to the nameless multitudes in all three countries that sent us information and names of contacts for this directory.

ACKNOWLEDGMENTS

[illegible]

[illegible]

[illegible]

[illegible]

CONTENTS

INTRODUCTION

Recent discussions about a proposed free trade agreement bridging Mexico, the United States, and Canada have awakened many North Americans to the ongoing economic integration in the region. Trade and investment across borders is increasing, but there is less awareness of a related phenomenon: the increased communication, organizing, and collaboration among the citizens of North America.

Although it lags behind economic integration, this social interaction is mounting in significance. From grassroots groups in border towns to labor union headquarters in New York, Toronto, and Mexico City, people are sharing experiences and ideas, fostering mutual understanding, and developing strategies to advance their interests. These social contacts are helping shape the new economic structures being built on the continent.

This directory seeks to promote expanded organizational contacts across the North American borders. It aims to broaden cross-border awareness and to facilitate access to binational and trinational initiatives in all walks of life. In this way, we hope to strengthen these initiatives and encourage the creation of new ones.

The Cross-Border Links Project began in November 1991 as a binational agreement between the Inter-Hemispheric Education Resource Center in the United States and Equipo Pueblo in Mexico. In addition, *Cross-Border Links* is co-sponsored by the Action Canada Network, resulting in a trinational research project.

Focusing on organizations with current activities involving bi/trinational relations, we examined almost 1,000 names of groups and people, sending a questionnaire to 450 organizations asking for information about their projects, resources, and any other pertinent data. We also repeatedly faxed and phoned to obtain necessary information. In some cases, when information was not available directly from the organization, we relied on other sources to compile the organizational profile.

Groups included in this directory vary greatly in their scope and perspective, ranging from prominent government agencies to recently formed grassroots groups, from business associations to labor organizations. To manage the disparity of groups with cross-border links, the directory is arranged by the primary focus of the organizations. We have organized the groups into eight categories: Networks for Fair Trade, Labor, Environment, Advocacy Organizations, Academic Institutions, Government Agencies,

Business Groups, and Electronic Networks. In this first edition, we did not include other institutions active in bi/trinational relations such as development foundations, media (TV programs, magazines), political parties, charitable organizations, churches, individuals (house or senate representatives, scholars, journalists, etc.), although there are a few exceptions. We should point out that there are a few other directories that may prove of interest to our readers. These include a directory of U.S.-Mexico border environmental groups published by the Border Ecology Project, a directory of Indian organizations published by the South and Meso American Indian Information Center, and a directory of nonprofit groups along the border available through the World Environment Center.

This edition of *Cross-Border Links* should be considered a first effort. We have sought to be as comprehensive and accurate as possible. But due to the tremendous difficulties obtaining detailed information about hundreds of groups, many of which have only recently been established, we are aware that there may be some omissions and errors. We apologize for any inaccuracies and encourage readers to help us make the second edition of *Cross-Border Links* (tentatively planned for late 1993) an improved publication by sending us updated information. At the rear of this directory is a questionnaire that will allow readers to 1) update or correct information on organizations already included in the directory, and 2) add other organizations that should be included in the second edition. We also suggest that you put the Cross-Border Links Project on your organization's mailing list for press releases and new publications. In this way, we will be able to update your profile and better promote your organization.

We finished the first edition of *Cross-Border Links* in June 1992 with the following totals:

Organizations that received the Cross-Border Links questionnaire: 450
Additional phone calls asking for direct information: 200
Total number of organizations listed: 260
Groups listed by activity:

- *Networks for Fair Trade: 12*
- *Labor: 53*
- *Environment: 39*
- *Advocacy Organizations: 58*
- *Academic Institutions: 49*
- *Government Agencies: 28*
- *Business Groups: 18*
- *Electronic Networks: 3*

Groups listed by country:

- *Canadian groups: 50*
- *Mexican groups: 60*
- *U.S. groups: 150*

*Groups listed that answered our questions (marked with an * after the name of the group): 200 = 76.9%*

Each profiled group includes address, phone, and contact person. The profile includes, when available, the following information: description of the group, activities and projects, links and affiliations, resources or publications, and the group's other offices and contacts. All prices listed are in local currencies unless otherwise specified. In the Networks for Fair Trade section we include a statement on free trade and a list of members for some of the organizations. These profiles were compiled by the staff of the Cross-Border Links Project from information provided by the groups themselves and through other research and interviews. We encourage readers to fill out the accompanying questionnaire and to write us with other suggestions for improving *Cross-Border Links*.

Ricardo Hernández & Edith Sánchez

Coordinators of the Cross-Border Links Project

PART I

Networks for Fair Trade

INTRODUCTION

The instigation of networks for fair trade between Canada, the United States, and Mexico is a popular response linked to the process of North American economic integration being promoted by the governments of all three countries under the banner of free trade. In fact, the first Canadian coalition opposed to free trade, the Pro-Canada Network, founded in 1987 and renamed Action Canada Network (ACN) in 1991, was a direct reaction to the free trade treaty between Canada and the United States. In the United States, two currents of popular organizing merged to form a fair trade movement. On the one hand were organizations that had been questioning the wisdom of the General Agreement on Tariffs and Trade (GATT) since 1985; on the other hand was a coalition that emerged in January 1991 to oppose the "fast track" of the free trade agreement. The Citizen Trade Watch Campaign, the Fair Trade Campaign, and Mobilization on Development, Trade, Labor and the Environment (MODTLE) are but three networks that resulted from this merger. They combine congressional lobbying with citizen education projects aimed at the formation of regional coalitions to scrutinize the proposed North American Free Trade Agreement (NAFTA).

The creation of binational networks between Mexico and the United States (exemplified by the Coalition for Justice in the Maquiladoras) was spawned by problems along the border associated with the *maquiladoras* and the environment, as well as by the probable exacerbating impact of free trade on such problems. Mexico City-based popular opposition to a free trade treaty was organized by the Mexican Action Network on Free Trade (RMALC) and originated within labor unions and other nongovernmental organizations (NGOs) with prior ties to groups in the United States and Canada such as the Authentic Labor Front, Common Frontiers (Mexico), People's Team, Woman to Woman, etc.

The basic thrust of the popular networks for fair trade is democratic participation in the definition of new commercial relationships between the three countries of North America. To this end, the networks seek to develop regional coalitions spanning the diversity of popular sectors in order to vocalize community problems within an alternative, more global vision of the process of economic integration. Network forums are enriched through bi/trinational sectoral exchange between labor, women, agricultural, and environmental groups. One seminal trinational encounter was the forum "Alternative Agenda to the Free Trade Agreement," held during October 1991 in Zacatecas, Mexico, and attended by 112 organizations from Canada (15), the United States (17), and Mexico (80, from 12 states of the Republic).

The fair trade networks employ a variety of tactics in the pursuit of their goals, such as: lobbying and direct political pressure on governments; grassroots educational projects to sensitize communities to the impacts of a free trade agreement; direct pressure on corporations that pollute the environment and/or whose labor conditions are detrimental to their workers; conducting alternative forums (Seattle, Toronto, Zacatecas, Montreal), parallel to the official meetings of government free trade negotiators; and analyzing government proposals in order to formulate and present viable alternatives.

The principal networks of the three countries differ in their capacity to mobilize the various sectors of society affected by the globalization of trade and commerce. In this respect, Action Canada Network has forged a broader coalition than its counterparts in the United States and Mexico. The absence of a unified popular movement in the United States to coordinate the work of more than eight major networks hampers chances of changing the politics of a free trade agreement. In Mexico, the RMALC lacks a nationwide scope, concentrating instead in sections of the North and in Mexico City. Networks in none of the three countries have adequately incorporated the informal, micro-industries, all of which will be affected by NAFTA. The networks compensate somewhat for these weaknesses by their sound analysis of NAFTA and by their continental perspective in the formulation of specific alternatives, the latter due largely to persistent Mexican input.

The relationship between the fair trade networks and the political parties is more estranged in the United States than in either Mexico or Canada. The New Democratic Party (NDP-Canada), and the Party of the Democratic Revolution (PRD-Mexico), are important elements of the opposition to NAFTA. Some network members consider an electoral victory by either of these parties as the most viable means of stopping any free trade treaty. However, the popular networks value their independence and claim no special relationship with any particular party. For example, in Mexico the RMALC supports Cuauhtémoc Cárdenas's proposal for a continental treaty for development as an alternative to NAFTA, yet the RMALC is not a branch of the PRD. On the other hand, The Other Economic Summit, a periodic, international political forum supported by the PRD and springing from an initial gathering in Houston in July 1990, shares a common agenda with the RMALC. Although the networks in the United States are not as associated with a political party as they are in Mexico, their links and legislative strategies are made almost exclusively with representatives of the Democratic Party. Even so, the U.S. networks have adopted a confrontive strategy of direct political pressure on government, in contrast to the indirect route afforded their Mexican counterparts by their closer relationship with a more genuinely oppositional political party—an avenue which complements the Mexican network's direct pressure activities.

In contrast to their more cautious approach in cultivating political party links, the networks for fair trade seek open support from labor unions, consumer and environmental groups, and NGOs that agree with their proposals. Such relationships can take the form of infrastructure sharing (office space, telephones, etc.), exchange of research and publications, or even direct economic support. This mutual aid occurs without compromising the network's autonomy, since the NGOs involved respect the decisions of the networks. Examples of this kind of cooperation can be seen between MODTLE and the International Labor Rights Education and Research Fund (ILRERF), between the Coalition for Justice in the Maquiladoras and the Interfaith Center on Corporate Responsibility, between the U.S.-Mexico-Canada Labor Solidarity Network and Labor Notes, between the RMALC and the Authentic Labor Front (FAT), and between Action Canada Network and the Canadian Centre for Policy Alternatives.

The networks opposing NAFTA are not alone in calling for fair trade. Opposition to NAFTA also stems from environmental coalitions, national labor unions, renowned academic centers, developmental organizations, and business sectors that would be adversely affected by a free trade agreement. Some of these groups are part of the networks for fair trade, while others share contacts and information. On the other hand, there are academic and business networks that have adopted a more favorable position toward free trade. Groups representative of all of these sectors are listed in other sections of the directory.

1. CANADA

Action Canada Network (ACN)*

251 Laurier Ave. W. #804
Ottawa, ON K1P 5J6
Phone: (613) 233-1764
Fax: (613) 233-1458
Email: (SoliNet) acn (PeaceNet will be connected in September 1992)
Contact: Tony Clarke, Chairperson

DESCRIPTION

ACN is a national, nonprofit, broadly based network of aboriginal, agricultural, church, cultural, environmental, peace, senior, trade union, feminist, antipoverty, development, and student organizations united in a campaign to promote a sustainable alternative to the current conservative agenda, particularly regarding free trade and unfair taxation. From its origins as the Pro-Canada Network (founded in May 1987 to fight the U.S.-Canada Free Trade Agreement), ACN has been dedicated to raising political awareness and mobilizing Canadian opposition to free trade. It promotes an alternative vision for Canada that puts people's needs before corporate profits. The network holds 3-4 national assemblies per year, but in addition, 9 out of the 10 Canadian provinces have independently functioning member coalitions. Working committees comprise education, finance, communications, and action.

STATEMENT ON FREE TRADE

"The United States is losing its dominance as free-market 'globalization' restructures our world. To consolidate its power, the Bush administration needs guaranteed access to an abundant supply of natural resources, on the one hand, and a large pool of cheap labour, on the other. The free trade deal with Canada provided the first, while a trade deal including Mexico will provide the second.

"The Action Canada Network is not advocating isolation. But we do object to the model of continental free trade that is being imposed on us—a model that is dominated by the interests of U.S. transnational corporations. Each nation must be able to exercise sovereignty over the development of its own natural resources to meet the needs of its own people. Trade should be a tool of development, not an end in itself."

RESOURCES

- *Action Canada Network-Dossier*. Of special interest are: *Dossier #29*, entitled *Inside Fortress North America*, and *Dossier #37*, *Inside Coalition Politics*, a guided tour of progressive coalition politics in Canada today.
- *We Can Say No*. A 28-minute video produced by Repeal the Deal Productions in British Columbia. A documentary linking what happened as a result of the bilateral free trade deal to the issues of NAFTA.

PROVINCIAL COALITIONS

Action Canada Network (British Columbia)
456 W. Broadway #211
Vancouver, BC V5Y 1R3
Phone: (604) 879-1209
Fax: (604) 520-5961
Contact: Jean Swanson

Action Canada Network (Alberta)
10451 170 St. #350
Edmonton, AB T5P 4T2
Phone: (403) 483-3021
Fax: (403) 484-5928
Email: (SoliNet) altafed
Contact: Lucien Royer

Action Canada Network (P.E.I.)
PO Box 1689
Charlottetown, PE C1A 7M4
Phone: (902) 892-1251
Fax: (902) 368-1644
Contact: Mary Boyd

CHO!CES: a coalition for social justice
PO Box 3852, Station B
Winnipeg, MB R2H 5H9
Phone: (204) 772-9691
Fax: (204) 775-6723
Contact: John Loxley

Coalition for Equality (Newfoundland and Labrador)
PO Box 18000
St. John's, Newfoundland A1C 6C2
Phone: (709) 753-2202
Fax: (709) 753-4110
Contact: Theresa MacKenzie

Metro (Halifax-Dartmouth) Coalition Against Free Trade
2039 A Creighton St.
Halifax, NS B3K 3R3
Phone: (902) 422-2130
Fax: (902) 466-6935
Contact: Paul Burgwin

Ontario Coalition for Social Justice
15 Gervais Dr. #407
Don Mills, ON M3C 1Y8
Phone: (416) 441-3663
Fax: (416) 445-8405
Contact: Mary Ann O'Connor

Saskatchewan Coalition for Social Justice
3525 Pasqua St.
Regina, SK S4S 7G9
Phone: (306) 586-6154
Fax: (306) 584-8714
Contact: Dave Durning

Solidarité populaire Québec
1600 Rue de Lorimier, local 107
Montreal, PQ H2K 3W5
Phone: (514) 768-3256
Fax: (514) 598-2400
Contact: Madeleine Parent or Marianne Roy

MEMBER ORGANIZATIONS

— Alliance of Canadian Cinema, Television, and Radio Artists
— Assembly of First Nations
— Canadian Auto Workers
— Canadian Brotherhood of Railway, Transport, and General Workers
— Canadian Environmental Law Association
— Canadian Federation of Students
— Canadian Labour Congress (and affiliated provincial federations of labour)
— Canadian Paperworkers Union
— Canadian Peace Alliance
— Canadian Teachers Federation
— Canadian Union of Postal Workers
— Canadian Union of Public Employees (CUPE)
— Centrale de l'enseignement du Québec
— Communications and Electrical Workers of Canada
— Confédération des syndicats nationaux (CSN)
— Confederation of Canadian Unions
— Council of Canadians
— Ecumenical Coalition for Economic Justice
— Graphic Communications International Union
— International Ladies' Garment Workers' Union
— Inter Pares
— Latin American Working Group
— National Action Committee on the Status of Women
— National Farmers Union
— National Federation of Nurses Unions
— National Pensioners and Senior Citizens Federation
— National Union of Public and General Employees
— One Voice Seniors Network
— OXFAM Canada
— Playwrights Union of Canada
— Public Service Alliance of Canada
— Rural Dignity of Canada
— Transportation and Communications International Union
— United Electrical, Radio, and Machine Workers of Canada
— United Food and Commercial Workers
— United Steelworkers of America.

Coalition québécoise sur les négociations trilatérales*

1601 Rue de Lorimier
Montreal, PQ H2K 4M5
Phone: (514) 598-2273
Fax: (514) 598-2052
Contact: Peter Bakvis, Confédération des syndicats nationaux

DESCRIPTION

The coalition is the offspring of those groups that actively opposed the free trade agreement during the 1988 bilateral negotiations between the United States and Canada. As yet adopting no specific position regarding NAFTA, Coalition québécoise researches the possible impact of a free trade agreement on the three negotiating countries, using the publications of member organizations to disseminate its information. One member, the Confédération des syndicats nationaux, is also an active member of Action Canada Network. Solidarité populaire Québec serves as an umbrella organization for the Coalition québécoise.

MEMBER ORGANIZATIONS

— Association médicale pour l'Amérique latine et les Caraibes (AMALC)

— Association québécoise des organismes de co-opération internationale (AQOCI)

— Centrale de l'enseignment du Québec (CEQ)

— Centre de documentation d'Amérique latine (CEDAL)

— Confédération des syndicats nationaux (CSN)

— CUSO-Québec

— Développement et paix

— Fédération des travailleurs et travailleuses du Québec (FTQ)

Common Frontiers*

11 Madison Ave.
Toronto, ON M5R 2S2
Phone: (416) 961-7847
Fax: (416) 924-5356
Email: (WEB) comfront
Contact: Ken Traynor

DESCRIPTION

This coalition of groups working on continental economic integration issues monitors NAFTA and the Enterprise for the Americas Initiative, and promotes trilateral links among popular-sector groups. Although engaging in some lobbying of the national government, Common Frontiers concentrates on serving as an ideas liaison through its office in Mexico (see p. 110), contacts in the United States, and its close relationship with Action Canada Network, and the Canadian Centre for Policy Alternatives.

RESOURCES

- *Bottom Line*. A 12-minute video touting the advantages from a corporate perspective of shifting production to a *maquiladora*.
- *Solidarity, Not Competition*. Proceedings from the conference on NAFTA organized by the Labour Council of Metro Toronto and York Region, May 1991. $10.

2. MEXICO

Red Mexicana de Acción Frente al Libre Comercio (RMALC)*

Godard 20
Col. Guadalupe Victoria
México, D.F. 07790
Phone: (5) 5-56-93-75/14
Fax: (5) 5-56-93-16
Email: (PeaceNet) igc:rmalc
Contact: Bertha Luján, Alejandro Quiróz or Manuel García Urrutia, members of the steering committee

DESCRIPTION

This network of organizations comprising labor, women, peasants, and environmentalists seeks to: 1) publish information about the economic integration of North America, its possible social costs, and suggested responses; 2) stimulate debate regarding the free trade agreement and its potential impacts; 3) guarantee national sovereignty and the social agenda of the common people; 4) develop cross-border links with similar social organizations in the United States and Canada. The RMALC hosted an international forum on alternatives to NAFTA (organized in conjunction with the Action Canada Network and MODTLE of the United States) in Zacatecas, Mexico, in October 1991 concurrent with the third official trilateral meeting of ministers negotiating NAFTA.

STATEMENT ON FREE TRADE

"Indispensible conditions for a regional economic integration agreement which is truly just and beneficial for the country are: a) an ample and democratic consultation with all potentially affected sectors, through a national referendum . . . sanctioned by an entity made up of Mexican citizens who are independent of the government; b) clear guarantees of our political independence and national sovereignty; c) true respect for the Political Constitution of Mexico and the national laws in relation to labor, foreign investments and intellectual property . . . ; g) adoption of the principle of equal pay for equal work in North America (a minimum wage applicable to the entire region); j) regional norms concerning the rational use of natural resources, the effective safe-guarding of the environment . . . and restrictions on the disposal of toxic wastes."

RESOURCES

- *Memoria de Zacatecas, Foro Internacional La Opinión Pública y el TLC: Alternativas Ciudadanas*. 248 pages. U.S. $8.
- *¿Libre Comercio o Explotación Libre?* 96 pages. July 1991. U.S. $4
- *Alternativas*. Monthly bulletin. U.S. $30/yr.

MEMBER ORGANIZATIONS

— Central Independiente de Obreros Agrícolas y Campesinos (CIOAC)

— Centro de Encuentros y Diálogos (CED)

— Centro de Estudios de Fronteras y Chicanos

— Centro de Investigación Laboral y Asesoría Sindical (CILAS)

— Coordinadora Nacional de Trabajadores de Aeroméxico

— ENLACE, Comunicación y Capacitación

— Equipo Pueblo

— Frente Auténtico del Trabajo (FAT)

— Frente Nacional de Abogados Democráticos

— Frente Patriótico Nacional (FPN)

— Frente Sindical Unitario (FSU)

— Fronteras Comunes/Centro Coordinador de Proyectos Ecuménicos (CECOPE)

— Grupo de Información y Estudios Migratorios

— Instituto de Investigaciones Sociales de la Universidad Nacional Autónoma de México (IIS-UNAM)

— Mujer a Mujer

— Pacto de Grupos Ecologistas

— Partido de la Revolución Democrática (PRD), Comisión Sindical

— Partido Revolucionario de los Trabajadores (PRT), Comisión Sindical

— Programa de Educación Laboral y Sindical/Sistematización de Experiencias del Movimiento Popular Mexicano (SEMPO)

— Seminario Permanente de Estudios Chicanos y de Fronteras

— Servicio, Desarrollo y Paz (SEDEPAC)

— Servicios Informativos Procesados (SIPRO)

— Sindicato 15 de Agosto de la Industria de la Confección

— Sindicato Belisario Domínguez de la Industria Textil

— Sindicato del Fideicomiso para Crédito en Areas de Riego y Temporal (SINTIFICART)

— Sindicato de Trabajadores de Imprenta Nuevo Mundo

— Sindicato de Trabajadores de la Universidad Iberoamericana

— Sindicato de Trabajadores de la Universidad Nacional Autónoma de México (STUNAM)

— Sindicato Independiente de Trabajadores de la Universidad Autónoma Metropolitana (SITUAM)

— Sindicato Insurgente Ignacio Allende de la Industria del Calzado

— Sindicato Nacional de Trabajadores de Elevadores Otis

— Sindicato Nacional de Trabajadores de Impulsora Mexicana de Telecomunicaciones

— Sindicato Nacional de Trabajadores de la Educación (SNTE), sección X

— Sindicato Nacional de Trabajadores de la Industria de la Costura, 19 de Septiembre

— Sindicato Nacional de Trabajadores de la Industria del Hierro y del Acero (SNTIHA)

— Sindicato Nacional de Trabajadores del Inca Rural (STINCA)

— Sindicato Nacional de Trabajadores Mineros, Sección Uno

— Sindicato Ricardo Flores Magón de HILSA

— Sindicato Unico de Trabajadores de la Secretaría de Pesca

— Sindicato Unico de Trabajadores de NOTIMEX (Agencia Mexicana de Noticias)

— Sindicato Unico de Trabajadores Universitarios (SUNTU)

— Unidad Cooperativa Independiente (UCI)

3. UNITED STATES

Citizen Trade Watch Campaign*

215 Pennsylvania Ave. SE
Washington, DC 20003
Phone: (202) 775-0531/546-4996
Fax: (202) 547-7392
Contact: Lori Wallach or Joe Tancredi, Media Relations

DESCRIPTION

This coalition of environmental, labor, consumer, religious, and farm organizations promotes a citizens' agenda regarding U.S. trade policy. The group emerged from an effort in May 1991 to stop the "fast track" extension, and later expanded its focus to include GATT and the U.S.-Mexico trade agreements. Citizen Trade Watch Campaign works closely with Public Citizen and the Fair Trade Campaign to promote congressional legislation and resolutions that ensure that citizens' interests in areas such as jobs, the environment, and consumer and worker safety are central to U.S. trade policy.

STATEMENT ON FREE TRADE

"We believe in expanding trade, but will not approve legislation to implement any trade agreement if such an agreement jeopardizes United States health, safety, labor, or environment laws."

RESOURCES

- *Everything You Always Wanted To Know About GATT, But Were Afraid To Ask.* A packet containing fact sheets, definitions of GATT terminology, and a bibliography and contact list. December 1991. Regular price: $5, member's price: $3.
- *Consumer and Environmental Analysis of the December 20, 1991 Uruguay Round GATT "Final Act" text.* A detailed analysis of how the GATT "Final Act" text undermines environmental protection and consumer safety. Regular price: $25, member's price: $20.
- *Trade Advisory Committees: Privileged Access for Polluters.* A report on how trade advisory committees operate in secret and are stacked with corporate representatives, thus closing consumers and other affected parties out of the process of trade negotiations. December 1991. Regular price: $25, member's price: $20.
- *Citizen Trade Watch Campaign Congressional Briefing Packet.* Includes position papers and background materials from consumer and environmental organizations. December 1991. Regular price: $15, member's price: $10.
- *The Consumer and Environmental Case Against Fast Track.* How fast track approval for international trade agreements endangers the environment and consumer safety. May 1991. Regular price: $7, member's price: $4.

Coalition for Fair Trade and Social Justice (CFTSJ)*

518 17th St. #200
Oakland, CA 94612
Phone: (510) 763-6584
Fax: (510) 763-4327
Email: (PeaceNet) igc:rlehman
Contact: Robert Lehman

DESCRIPTION

This regional coalition unites labor, environmental, immigrant rights, human rights, family farm, Latino, and church organizations concerned about the social and ecological impacts of trade and investment. It engages in lobbying, public education, and establishing links between organizations in Northern California and similar groups throughout North America. The CFTSJ promotes equitable, ecological development as the basis for an alternative to free trade ideology. In February 1992, the coalition organized a conference in Berkeley entitled "Facing Free Trade Together."

Coalition for Justice in the Maquiladoras (CJM)*

3120 W. Ashby
San Antonio, TX 78228
Phone: (210) 732-8957
Fax: (210) 732-8324
Contact: Susan Mika

DESCRIPTION

The CJM is a binational coalition of religious, environmental, labor, Latino, and women's organizations seeking to pressure U.S. transnational corporations to adopt socially responsible practices within the *maquiladora* industry to ensure a clean environment on both sides of the border, safe working conditions inside the *maquila* plants, and a fair standard of living for the industry's workers. The group promotes the Maquiladora Standards of Conduct, a code that requires corporations to alleviate critical problems that their activities create.

STATEMENT ON FREE TRADE

"The Maquiladora Standards of Conduct are the least common denominator which must be addressed for a trade agreement to have credibility in a situation where what is morally wrong in the United States is wrong in Mexico, too."

RESOURCES

- *CJM Newsletter*. Bimonthly. $15 to groups in CJM, $20 to nonmembers.
- *Maquiladora Standards of Conduct*. Document. Price varies depending on number purchased.
- *Maquiladoras: A Broken Promise*. A collection of stories from newspapers articles about toxic chemical accidents, fires, and problems in plants in the Matamoros area. Edited by AFL-CIO.
- Packet of clippings on topics such as the EPA/SEDUE hearings and *maquiladora* activities available upon request for $1 each.

MEMBER ORGANIZATIONS

- A la Vida, Boston
- Amalgamated Clothing and Textile Workers Union (ACTWU)
- American Federation of Labor-Congress of Industrial Organizations (AFL-CIO)
- American Friends Service Committee
- Archdiocese of San Antonio, Presbyterial Council
- Benedictine Resource Center, San Antonio
- Benedictine Sisters, Boerne, Texas
- Brigidine Sisters, San Antonio
- Catalyst, Vermont
- Central America Resource Center
- Christian Brothers Investment Services, Inc.
- Church Women United
- Clean Water Action
- Comité de Apoyo
- Comité Fronterizo de Obreras
- Commission on Religion in Appalachia
- Communications Workers of America
- Congregation of the Holy Cross, Eastern Province
- Despacho Obrero
- Diocese of San Angelo
- Dominican Sisters, Houston
- Dominican Sisters of the Sick Poor
- Environmental Health Coalition
- Fair Trade Campaign
- Federation for Industrial Retention and Renewal
- Friars of Atonement
- Friends of the Earth
- Glenmary Home Missioners
- Illinois Coalition for Responsible Investment
- Institute for Mission in the U.S.A., ELCA
- Institute for Policy Studies/Third World Women's Project
- Interfaith Center on Corporate Responsibility, Equality Issue Group
- Inter-Hemispheric Education Resource Center
- International Brotherhood of Electrical Workers
- International Labor Rights Education and Research Fund
- International Ladies' Garment Workers' Union
- International Union of Electronic Workers (IUE)
- Iowa/Wisconsin/Minnesota Coalition for Responsible Investment
- Justice and Peace Action Forum, Houston
- Kansas City Maquiladora Task Force
- Labor Council for Latin American Advancement
- Leadership Conference of Women Religious, Region XII (TX, AR, AZ, NM)
- Maricopa County Organizing Project, Phoenix
- Methodist Federation for Social Action
- Midwest Coalition for Responsible Investment, St. Louis
- National Lawyers Guild Labor and Employment Committee
- National Lawyers Guild/Toxics Committee

— National Organization for Women
— National Organization for Women, Austin Chapter
— National Toxics Campaign
— National Toxics Campaign Fund
— New Mexico Conference of Churches
— Office for Justice and Peace, San Diego Catholic Diocese
— Our Lady of Victory Missionary Sisters
— Pesticide Action Network, North America Regional Center
— Philadelphia Area Coalition for Responsible Investment
— Priests of the Sacred Heart
— Project Earth
— Province of Saint Augustine, Capuchin-Franciscan
— Santa Clara Center for Occupational Safety and Health
— School Sisters of Notre Dame, Dallas Province
— Sinsinawa Dominicans
— Sisters of Charity of Cincinnati, Western Region
— Sisters of Charity of St. Elizabeth, Ethics for Investments Committee
— Sisters of Charity of the Incarnate Word, San Antonio
— Sisters of Divine Providence, San Antonio
— Sisters of Loretto
— Sisters of Mercy, St. Louis
— Sisters of St. Benedict, Oklahoma City
— Sisters of St. Mary of Namur, Eastern Province
— Society of Mary, Province of St. Louis
— Southwest Network for Economic and Environmental Justice
— Southwest Organizing Project
— Southwest Public Workers Union
— Texans United
— Texas Center for Policy Studies
— Texas Conference of Churches
— Transportation Communications Union
— Trinity Chicano Coalition
— Tri-State Coalition for Responsible Investment
— Tucsonians for a Clean Environment
— UAW, International Union
— United Methodist Church, General Board of Church and Society
— United Methodist Church, General Board of Global Ministries, Women's Division
— United Methodist Church, National Division
— Urban Bishops Coalition of the Episcopal Church
— YWCA of the U.S.A. National Board

Fair Trade Campaign*

Western Regional Office
425 Mississippi St.
San Francisco, CA 94107
Phone: (415) 826-6314
Fax: (415) 826-5303
Contact: Craig Merrilees, National Co-Director

DESCRIPTION

This coalition of consumer, labor, environmental, and family-farm organizations promotes trade policy based on the principles of economic and social justice. The Fair Trade Campaign organizes protests and events to influence GATT and NAFTA. It works closely with counterparts in Japan, Europe, Mexico, and other nations, and in the United States coordinates with the Citizen Trade Watch Campaign and with the Coalition for Justice in the Maquiladoras.

RESOURCES

- *Alerts*. Single-page bulletin issued several times a month, only for activists.
- *Updates*. Approximately 4 per year, more often when needed.
- *Border Trouble: Rivers in Peril*. A report on water pollution stemming from industrial development along the U.S.-Mexico border, published by the National Toxics Campaign in May 1991. $5.
- *Impact of the Mexico Trade Agreement on Consumers and the Environment*. Testimony by Craig Merrilees on behalf of the Fair Trade Campaign, April 1991. 9 pages. $1.
- *Senate Resolution 109 Means Action on the President's Promises*. 1991.

OTHER OFFICES

Midwest Regional Office
220 S. State St. #714
Chicago, IL 60604
Phone: (312) 341-4713
Fax: (312) 341-4716
Email: iatp
Contact: Don Wiener, National Co-Director

Eastern Regional Office
410 W. 25th St.
New York, NY 10001
Phone: (212) 627-2314
Fax: (212) 366-4312
Contact: Nikos Valance

Southern Regional Office c/o Public Citizen
233 Mitchell St. SW #525
Atlanta, GA 30303
Phone: (404) 524-4116
Fax: (404) 524-4116

Mountain Regional Office
1071 Madison St.
Denver, CO 80206
Phone: (303) 393-1870
Fax: (303) 399-9263

Federation for Industrial Retention and Renewal (FIRR)*

3411 W. Diversey #10
Chicago, IL 60647
Phone: (312) 252-8797
Fax: (312) 278-5918
Contact: Jim Benn, Executive Director

DESCRIPTION

FIRR is a nationwide federation of community-based organizations challenging deindustrialization, capital flight and its resulting poverty with economic development strategies that introduce community into the decisionmaking process. Federation affiliates seek to build local coalitions of religious, labor, trade, environmental, and conversion activists in order to target conditions in the *maquiladoras*, connect those conditions with collapsing standards in U.S. industrial communities, and link those communities to national strategies. Specific issues of focus include regional planning, worker training tied to job development, plant-closings law, industrial capital funds, and trade. FIRR is affiliated with the Coalition for Justice in the Maquiladoras, the Fair Trade Campaign, the Financial Democracy Campaign, and the Campaign for Responsible Technology.

STATEMENT ON FREE TRADE

"We believe that 'free' trade agreements serve only the short-term profit goals of those corporations capable of taking the greatest advantage of relocation and outsourcing uses of new technology. By sacrificing the democratic traditions of our communities, as well as socially responsible strategic industrial development to the altar of the market place, 'free' trade is arguing that profit holds preference over social value. This narrow focus has only the most destructive potential for working people and their communities."

RESOURCES

- *FIRR News*. Quarterly newsletter.
- *FIRR Alert*. Bimonthly.
- *State and Local Initiatives in Plant Closings Legislation*.

MEMBER ORGANIZATIONS

— Calumet Project for Industrial Jobs, Chicago, IL

— Center for Neighborhood Technology, Chicago, IL

— Cleveland Coalition Against Plant Closings, Cleveland, OH

— Coalition for Economic Justice, Buffalo, NY

— Coalition for Fair Trade and Economic Justice/Plant Closures Project, Oakland, CA

— CommonWorks, Syracuse, NY

— Community Economic Stabilization Corp., Portland, OR

— Fuerza Unida, San Antonio, TX

- Hometowns Against Shutdowns, Freehold, NJ
- ICA Group, Boston, MA
- Jobs with Peace, Philadelphia, PA
- La Mujer Obrera, El Paso, TX
- Machine Action Project, Springfield, MA
- Merrimack Valley Project, Lawrence, MA
- Midwest Center for Labor Research, Chicago, IL
- Naugatuck Valley Project, Waterbury, CT
- Ohio Valley Industrial Retention and Renewal Project, Wheeling, WV
- Puget Sound Cooperative Federation, Seattle, WA
- Religion and Labor Council of Kansas City, MO
- Seattle Worker Center, WA
- South Chicago Jobs Authority, Chicago, IL
- Southerners for Economic Justice, Durham, NC
- Steel Valley Authority, Homestead, PA
- Tennessee Industrial Renewal Network, Knoxville, TN
- Tomkins-Cortland Labor Coalition, Ithaca, NY
- Tri-State Conference, Pittsburgh, PA
- Tri-State Economic Justice Network, Newark, NJ
- Working Group on Economic Dislocation, St. Paul, MN

Minnesota Fair Trade Coalition*

821 Raymond Ave. #160
Saint Paul, MN 55114
Phone: (612) 644-4472
Fax: (612) 644-9331
Contact: James Mangan, Working Group on Economic Dislocation

DESCRIPTION

This regional coalition of labor, environmental, social justice, and agricultural groups opposes the free trade agenda through education and political pressure, promoting "fair" as opposed to "free" trade. It researches the likely impact of NAFTA on Minnesota's communities, jobs, farmers, consumers, and environment.

Mobilization on Development, Trade, Labor and the Environment (MODTLE)* — name changed to Alliance for Responsible Trade (ART)

PO Box 74
100 Maryland Ave. NE
Washington, DC 20002
Phone: (202) 544-7198
Fax: (202) 543-5999
Email: (PeaceNet) cdp:laborrights
Contact: Pharis Harvey, Coordinator

DESCRIPTION

Initiated in January 1991 with a forum organized by the International Labor Rights Education and Research Fund (ILRERF), MODTLE is a loose-knit coalition of labor, environmental, consumer, religious, agricultural, human rights, and development groups unified around opposition to the free trade agenda. The coalition comprises nongovernmental organizations dedicated to ensuring that any trade agreements negotiated by the United States will include provisions to protect labor and human rights, preserve community integrity, and safeguard the environment. In conjunction with the Action Canada Network and the Mexican Action Network on Free Trade, MODTLE has sponsored trinational public forums to encourage public debate regarding NAFTA.

STATEMENT ON FREE TRADE

From its alternative agenda for NAFTA: "The ultimate objective of any North American agreement should be to lift the living standards of the 380 million people of the three nations through a continental development initiative. Trade and investment—the main areas addressed in the proposed agreement—should not be seen as ends in themselves, but as tools toward development, social justice and a healthy environment."

RESOURCES

- *Final Declaration of the International Forum "Public Opinion and the Free Trade Negotiations—Citizens' Alternatives."* Zacatecas, Mexico, 1992.
- *Development and Trade Strategies for North America.* An alternative agenda for the NAFTA endorsed by 48 organizations in the United States. Includes Agreement Objectives; Environmental and Consumer Protection Framework; Labor Rights and Standards; Human Rights; Agricultural Issues; Funding Mechanisms for Raising Standards under NAFTA; and Enforcement Mechanisms to Ensure Compliance with Environmental, Labor Rights and Human Rights Obligations. March 1992.

MEMBERS OF THE STEERING COMMITTEE

— Pharis Harvey, ILRERF

— Steve Hellinger and Karen Hansen-Kuhn, Development GAP

— Thea Lee, Economic Policy Institute

— John Cavanagh, Institute for Policy Studies

— Elmira Nazombe, Interfaith Impact for Justice and Peace

— Cameron Duncan, Greenpeace

— Bob Kingsley, United Electrical, Radio, and Machine Workers of America (UE)

Organizations listed for identification purposes.

U.S.-Mexico-Canada Labor Solidarity Network*

— name changed to North American Worker-to-Worker Network (NAWWN)

PO Box 6003
Durham, NC 27708
Phone: (919) 286-5617
Email: (PeaceNet) cdp:carnet.mexnews
Contact: Jackie van Anda, Coordinator

DESCRIPTION

Focusing on the need for ongoing solidarity and exchange, grassroots education, and trinational actions, the network: 1) exchanges information, ideas, and support with democratic and independent labor movements in Mexico and its counterparts in Canada; 2) organizes and supports activities that increase awareness among union members and the general public of the common interests shared by working people in all three countries; 3) organizes and supports actions that pressure transnational corporations and the three governments on such issues as living and working conditions, job security, environmental and occupational health, women's rights, public services for human needs, and economic and political democracy; and 4) provides grassroots organizations and individuals a way to share resources and avoid duplication of effort.

RESOURCES

- *Electronic mailings and information packets* about events, materials, news and analysis related to issues of free trade in the United States, Mexico, and Canada. Bimonthly.

MEMBERS OF THE STEERING COMMITTEE

— Tom Laney, MEXUSCAN Solidarity Task Force, UAW 879

— Karyl Dunson, Director, Texas Committee on Occupational Safety and Health

— Ben Davis, Labor Coalition on Central America

— Bob Kingsley, Political Action Director, United Electrical, Radio, and Machine Workers of America (UE)

— Joe Fahey, President, Teamsters Union, Local 912

— Bob Peterson, Co-Chair, National Coalition of Education Activists

— Mary McGinn, Labor Notes

— Dan Leahy, Labor Center, Evergreen State College

Organizations listed for identification purposes.

PART II

Labor

INTRODUCTION

In no social sector has the proposed North American Free Trade Agreement (NAFTA) produced greater changes in attitudes and cross-border relations than in organized labor. For businesses NAFTA largely represents a mere formalization of ongoing continental integration. For government agencies the changes occurred before NAFTA was considered a possibility, with the back-to-back inaugurations of presidents Salinas and Bush. But for labor unions and federations, NAFTA is a concrete target for legislative action, a rallying point for rank-and-file mobilization, and a spur to the creation or deepening of alliances with cross-border counterparts. Many labor activists have long argued that international solidarity is the only effective response to global capitalism. Unwittingly, Presidents Bush and Salinas have provided the platform for that message to spread well beyond the inner circles of unions and labor scholars.

The prognosis for the labor movement is anything but rosy, however. Unions' influence within the Mexican, United States, and Canadian political systems has declined over the last decade—precipitously, in the cases of the United States and Mexico. Serious schisms exist within several large North American unions over questions of internal democracy, union-management relations, and appropriate international strategy. A seemingly insurmountable political gap also separates the pro-NAFTA, government-affiliated unions of Mexico—representing the vast majority of that country's organized workers—from their northern counterparts, who seek to alter or defeat NAFTA.

The disagreement over free trade has led U.S. unions to break with longstanding policy and pursue overt contact with Mexico's independent labor organizations. This policy change may also have been encouraged by annual binational and trinational labor exchanges (see Mexico-U.S. Dialogos), which for the last five years have allowed union officials to meet in private with other unionists of all stripes. But the new contacts do not go far enough for many rank-and-file activists in the three countries. Associated for the most part with dissident movements within their own unions, these activists seek far greater support from U.S. and Canadian labor organizations for the democratic labor movement in Mexico. Such support would constitute interference in the internal matters of other unions, argue U.S. union officials. Furthermore, they contend, it is not always clear who is in the right in many labor disputes, nor what the political consequences of foreign involvement might be.

Whether and how unions work out these questions is a matter of great import. The opportunity to shape the future of trading blocs, to create standards and institutions for the protection of labor rights, has presented itself in North America as it did in Europe. To persuade this continent's governments to adopt a social charter similar to that of the European Community will require strong trinational coalitions, within which labor unions will be crucial.

1. CANADA

British Columbia Trade Union Group (TUG)*

310 Triumph St.
Vancouver, BC V5K 1V1
Phone: (604) 298-6301/872-3092
Fax: (604) 872-0709
Contact: Bill Brassington

DESCRIPTION

The B.C. Trade Union Group is a volunteer organization of union members that seeks to establish worker-to-worker and union-to-union projects to develop solidarity and alternatives to free trade and structural adjustment.

ACTIVITIES

TUG organizes tours of *maquiladoras* in order to create a better understanding of free trade and related issues, to provide participants with background information, and to mobilize and educate union members.

LINKS

TUG maintains working relationships with Action Canada Network, Common Frontiers, Latin American Working Group, and Saskatchewan International Labour Program.

RESOURCES

- *When They Win, We Win*. A labor information kit about Central America, women in the *maquiladoras*, and health and environment on the U.S.-Mexico border.
- *Crossing the Line: Canada and Free Trade with Mexico*. Edited by Jim Sinclair (Vancouver: New Star Books, 1992). $15.95.
- *Central America Update*. Monthly.

Canadian Auto Workers (CAW)*

205 Placer Court, North York
Willowdale, ON M4E 1Y9
Phone: (416) 495-3757/6548
Fax: (416) 495-6564/59
Contact: Tony Wohlfarth

DESCRIPTION

The CAW represents workers in the auto assembly and parts industries, as well as in aerospace, communications, electronics, and railways. It broke from the United Auto Workers in the early 1980s in response to the UAW's decision to pursue closer union-management cooperation. The CAW's harder line is also evident in its leadership within Canada to establish links with independent Mexican labor groups. Both independently and through Common Frontiers and Action Canada Network, the union has begun to network on issues such as the *maquiladoras*, free trade, the Enterprise for the Americas Initiative, and the struggle for union democracy in Mexico.

RESOURCES

- *Contact*. Weekly. Free.
- *Union Magazine*. Quarterly. Free.

Canadian Labour Congress (CLC)*

2841 Riverside Dr.
Ottawa, ON K1V 8X7
Phone: (613) 521-3400
Fax: (613) 521-4655
Contact: Andrew Jackson

DESCRIPTION

The Canadian Labour Congress is the umbrella group for 151 unions and 12 federations of labor representing 2.2 million Canadians. It argued vigorously against the U.S.-Canada Free Trade Agreement, and has worked for its abrogation since it was signed in 1989. The CLC's research department has compiled an extensive list of plant shutdowns and production cutbacks that they attribute to the agreement.

At the CLC's biennial convention in June 1992, an action program on NAFTA was presented. Details were unavailable as of press time.

Canadian Union of Public Employees (CUPE)*

21 rue Florence St.
Ottawa, ON K2P 0W6
Phone: (613) 237-1590
Fax: (613) 237-5508
Email: (SoliNet)
Contact: Larry Katz, National Research Director, or John Calvert, Senior Research Officer

DESCRIPTION

CUPE represents over 400,000 workers in all ten provinces, making it Canada's largest union. It has not actively sought to establish cross-border links, but it has supported the Common Frontiers and Action Canada Network initiatives to oppose NAFTA, and to facilitate linkages between labor and popular organizations in Canada and Latin America. CUPE also co-sponsors the Saskatchewan International Labour Program.

RESOURCES

- *The Leader*. Newsletter.
- *The Facts*. Bimonthly journal analyzing economic and labor issues, including free trade. (Free to members, complimentary to selected readers.)

Centrale de l'enseignement du Québec

9405 rue Sherbrooke Est
Montreal, PQ H1L 6P3
(514) 356-8888
Contact: Richard Langlois

Communications and Electrical Workers of Canada (CWC)*

25 Cecil St., 2nd Floor
Toronto, ON M5T 1N1
Phone: (416) 977-6678
Fax: (416) 977-4338
Contact: Glenn Pattinson, Vice-President (Industrial Sector), or Richard Long, Vice-President (Ontario Region)

DESCRIPTION

The CWC represents telecommunications workers across Canada, and electrical manufacturing workers throughout Ontario. Its international solidarity work began several years ago with the Northern Telecom International Solidarity Coalition. This is an alliance of unions from 8 countries including the United States but not Mexico, where Northern Telecom has two nonunion plants. It was formed to pressure management at Northern Telecom to improve labor relations.

ACTIVITIES

Recently the CWC demonstrated the effectiveness of such solidarity work by threatening Northern Telecom's management with trouble in Canada if it didn't settle a conflict with unionized workers in the New England region of the United States. A settlement was reached soon thereafter.

In early 1992 the CWC signed an alliance with the Communications Workers of America and the Union of Mexican Telephone Workers (STRM—see p. 40). The agreement recognizes the difficulty of establishing joint positions among unions with varying political and technological positions. The three signatories committed themselves to "the permanent exchange of trade union information," and, "when necessary and possible," to "support joint mobilization."

Confédération des syndicats nationaux (CSN)*

1601 Ave. de Lorimier
Montreal, PQ H2K 4M5
Phone: (514) 598-2262
Fax: (514) 598-2052
Contact: Peter Bakvis, International Relations Service

DESCRIPTION

The CSN is a national organization of labor unions, federations, and central councils. It is not affiliated with any political party.

LINKS

It is member of Action Canada Network and the Coalition québécoise sur les négociations trilatérales.

International Ladies' Garment Workers' Union (ILGWU)*

Ontario District Council
33 Cecil St. #2
Toronto, ON M5T 1N1
Phone: (416) 977-1384
Fax: (416) 977-6999
Contact: Alexandra Dagg

DESCRIPTION

The ILGWU represents workers in the garment industry. Representatives have attended trilateral conferences opposed to NAFTA.

RESOURCES

- *Fabric*. Bimonthly newsletter. Free.

Labor Links Solidarity Committee

356 Queens Avenue
London, ON N6B 1X6

ACTIVITIES

Labor Links organized "Our Common Cause, Our Common Future: Working Together to Make a Difference," a trinational conference in May 1992 that focused on strengthening links between grassroots organizations in order to devise alternatives to the corporate agenda.

Saskatchewan International Labour Program (SILP)*

136 Ave. F South
Saskatoon, SK S7M 1S8
Phone: (306) 653-2250
Fax: (306) 652-8377
Contact: Bill Robb

DESCRIPTION

SILP provides education on international development and promotes international labor solidarity. Sponsored by OXFAM-Canada, CUPE, and other organizations, SILP hosts an annual conference and outreach program for provincial union members on structural adjustment, including NAFTA.

RESOURCES

- *Solidarity News*. Quarterly newsletter.

Telecommunications Workers Union*

5261 Lane St.
Burnaby, BC V5H 4A6
Phone: (604) 437-4822
Fax: (604) 435-7760
Contact: Sid Shniad, Research Director

DESCRIPTION

The Telecommunications Workers Union represents 11,000 telephone workers in British Columbia. Representatives have pursued contacts with unionists and activists in Mexico both regarding NAFTA and concerning the privatization and deregulation of Mexico's telecommunications industry, with the goal of better coordinating labor's response to the international restructuring of capital.

LINKS

Active in Action Canada Network, the union is also affiliated with the Canadian Labour Congress; the British Columbia Federation of Labour; and the Postal, Telegraph and Telephone International trade union secretariat.

RESOURCES

- *The Transmitter*. Newsletter issued 8 times per year.

United Electrical, Radio, and Machine Workers of Canada (UE-Canada)

10 Codeco Court
Don Mills, ON M3A 1A2
Phone: (416) 447-5196
Contact: Joan McNeil

ACTIVITIES

Most of the UE's international solidarity work occurs in the United States, but the Canadian section has also become involved. In June 1992, UE representatives from Canada and the United States met with officials of the Canadian Auto Workers and the Mexican Electricians Union (SME) at the latter's office in Mexico to formulate a joint position vis-à-vis NAFTA and the *maquiladoras*. No agreement has been reached on NAFTA—the SME supports the process while the other participants oppose it—but common ground was discovered regarding regulation of *maquiladoras*.

United Fishermen and Allied Workers Union

111 Victoria Dr. #160
Vancouver, BC V5L 4C4
Phone: (604) 255-1336
Contact: Jim Sinclair

DESCRIPTION

Members of this union have been hit hard by the U.S.-Canada Free Trade Agreement, which opened the door to lower-cost U.S. processing of raw fish caught in Canada. Union activists have shared this experience with Mexican counterparts in the Ministry of Fishing Workers Union (Sindicato Unico de Trabajadores de la Secretaría de Pesca).

2. MEXICO

Centro de Investigación Laboral y Asesoría Sindical (CILAS)*

Dr. Liceaga 180 A-5, despacho 1001
Col. Doctores
México, D.F.
Phone: (5) 5-78-72-97
Fax: (5) 5-78-72-97
Contact: Luis Bueno Rodríguez, Director, or Raquél Ochoa

DESCRIPTION

CILAS conducts research on labor and economic issues and provides consultation on questions of labor law, occupational health and safety, training, and the formation of labor groups. Although rooted in the textile, telecommunications, and education industries, its most active international work is helping to organize the Trinational Automotive Coordinating Committee. The center is a member of the Mexican Action Network on Free Trade (RMALC), and coordinates research on NAFTA, information exchanges among labor groups, and public education activities related to NAFTA.

Confederación de Trabajadores de México (CTM)

Vallarta 8
Col. Tabacalera
México, D.F. 06470
Phone: (5) 7-05-10-91/09-66
Contact: Tomás Martínez

DESCRIPTION

The CTM is the largest union federation in Mexico, claiming five million members in 14,000 unions. Although its membership is probably closer to two million workers, the CTM remains the country's most important labor organization, and its 93-year-old leader, Fidel Velázquez, continues to dominate the Labor Congress, which represents all Mexican workers at government policymaking negotiating sessions.

For decades the CTM and its member unions were almost the only labor organizations in Mexico with which major U.S. or Canadian unions had relations. But the CTM's pro-NAFTA stance, and Velázquez's visits to the United States and Canada to preach free trade's virtues have opened a gap between the CTM and its northern counterparts. Velázquez himself has rejected bi/trinational cooperation on trade issues, stating that the fundamentally opposed perspectives of unions in the three countries preclude the possibility of finding common goals toward which to work. This contrasts with the stance of the non-CTM telephone workers union (STRM), which favors free trade but also signed an alliance with communication workers' unions in Canada and the United States.

Despacho Obrero

Isaac Newton 936
Col. Del Futuro
Ciudad Juárez, Chih.
Phone: (16) 18-43-77
Contact: Gustavo de la Rosa Hickerson

DESCRIPTION

Despacho Obrero (Workers' Bureau) is an organization of lawyers that provides consultation and assistance to workers involved in individual and/or collective labor conflicts along the northern border. The office maintains files on border issues and a list of toxic releases by the *maquiladoras*. Through its Worker Community (Comunidad Obrera) project, Despacho is attempting to broaden its scope to include worker training on the Federal Labor Law, occupational health and safety, and the handling of toxic materials. The project also seeks to establish a labor-based policy on environmental protection.

LINKS

Despacho Obrero is a member of the Coalition for Justice in the Maquiladoras.

Frente Auténtico del Trabajo (FAT)*

Godard 20
Col. Guadalupe Victoria
México, D.F. 07790
Phone: (5) 5-56-93-75/14
Fax: (5) 5-56-93-16
Email: (PeaceNet) igc:rmalc
Contact: Bertha E. Luján, Benedicto Martínez, or Antonio Velásquez, National Coordinators

DESCRIPTION

The FAT is the most important independent labor organization in the country, with 30 years of experience and some 40,000 members. It is also the primary vehicle for increased ties with U.S. and Canadian unions within Mexican labor. The FAT has provided an alternative to the CTM for a wide range of U.S. and Canadian unions seeking partners in the effort to modify or defeat NAFTA, including the AFL-CIO, the ACTWU, the UAW and the UE. These contacts have in turn strengthened the FAT's domestic position by deterring government and official-union repression, and in some cases by producing funds for organizing work.

Despite these achievements, the FAT remains far smaller than its progovernment counterparts, and hardly an equal in resources and political weight to its new allies in the Canadian and U.S. movements.

ACTIVITIES

The FAT was a driving force behind the October 1990 labor conference in Cuernavaca, at which Mexican unionists heard first hand from Canadians about the effects of the U.S.-Canada Free Trade Agreement and the dangers of NAFTA. Since then the FAT has continued to help organize trinational conferences and has gained increased media exposure.

LINKS

The FAT was one of the principal founders of the Mexican Action Network on Free Trade (RMALC).

RESOURCES

- *Resistencia Obrera*. Quarterly magazine. U.S. $10.

Movimiento Democrático de los Trabajadores de la Ford

c/o Centro de Investigación Laboral y Asesoría Sindical (CILAS)
Dr. Liceaga 180 A-5, despacho 1001
Col. Doctores
México, D.F.
Phone: (5) 5-78-72-97
Fax: (5) 5-78-72-97
Contact: Raúl Escobar

DESCRIPTION

Movimiento Democrático de los Trabajadores de la Ford (Ford Workers Democratic Movement) was a short-lived but important insurrection within the government-affiliated Ford Workers Union occurring from 1988 to 1991. Members of the movement—centered at Ford's assembly plant in Cuautitlán, just north of Mexico City—sought the right to freely choose their union representatives. Apparent collaboration among the company, union leaders, and the government effectively repressed the movement through a combination of election fraud, mass firings, and physical intimidation, including murder. Despite its ultimate defeat, the struggle served as a catalyst for increased interest on the part of U.S. and Canadian unionists in labor rights in Mexico.

ACTIVITIES

Representatives of the movement have attended bi/trinational labor conferences and visited numerous union locals in the United States and Canada in order to discuss both their experience and labor rights in Mexico.

Mujeres en Acción Sindical (MAS)

Aragón 122
Col. Alamos
Mexico D.F. 03400
Phone: (5) 5-19-80-48
Contact: Patricia Mercado

ACTIVITIES

MAS organizes national and international conferences about the position of women in the economy and the labor movement. In February 1992 it collaborated with Mujer a Mujer to sponsor a trinational women's conference outside of Mexico City on economic integration and NAFTA. It also participated in the trinational conference on NAFTA in Zacatecas in October 1991.

Programa de Educación Laboral y Sindical (SEMPO)*

Valladolid 33
Col. Roma
México, D.F. 05700
Phone: (5) 2-07-80-19/5-25-22-36
Fax: (5) 5-84-38-95
Contact: José Antonio Vital Galicia

DESCRIPTION

Programa de Educación Laboral y Sindical (the Program of Labor and Union Education) arose in 1982 as a project of the Center for Ecumenical Studies, which launched the group in order to research the labor movement and develop coordination strategies.

ACTIVITIES

SEMPO inaugurated the Program for Mexico-U.S.-Canada Labor Interchange, which seeks to encourage contacts and coordination among the workers of Mexico, the United States, and Canada by providing assistance for international communication and union exchanges. It also runs a data center and conducts research into migration, *maquiladoras*, occupational health, wages and productivity, human rights, and union organization.

SEMPO has organized two trilateral "Common Interests" labor conferences in Mexico. The second of these, held in October 1991 in the state of Puebla, produced a "Charter of Labor, Social, and Human Rights for Mexican, U.S., and Canadian Workers."

LINKS

SEMPO is a member of the Mexican Action Network on Free Trade (RMALC).

RESOURCES

- *Tratado de Libre Comercio*. A monthly bulletin.
- *Workers and the NAFTA, Conclusions of the Union Interchange II Mexico-U.S.-Canada*. October 1991, Metepec, Puebla.
- *El TLC y los Trabajadores*. Forthcoming.

Sindicato de Telefonistas de la República Mexicana (STRM)

Villalongín 50
México, D.F.
Phone: (5) 5-66-12-27/46-45-05
Contact: Francisco Hernández Juárez, Secretary General

DESCRIPTION

The STRM and the Mexican Electricians Union (SME) were the two most important founding members of the Mexican Federation of Unions of Goods and Services (FESEBES) in 1990. This federation was touted by many as the forerunner of a "modernized" labor movement in Mexico, free of corruption, relatively democratic, and willing to cooperate with management and the government in the technological modernization of the country. The STRM has provided strong support for the Mexican government, and has agreed to "modernization on the government's terms" in the words of its critics, even when that has meant job loss for a majority of the union's members. To a greater degree than either the FAT or the CTM, Hernández Juárez has succeeded in gaining access to NAFTA negotiations—especially in the telecommunications sector—though the union appears to have little influence over the outcome.

The STRM signed an alliance with its U.S. and Canadian counterparts (CWA and CWC) in February 1992 despite differences in their views on NAFTA. The three signatories committed themselves to "the permanent exchange of trade union information," and, "when necessary and possible," to "support joint mobilization."

The STRM's progovernment, pro-NAFTA stance has produced a sizeable dissident movement within the union, but this movement appears to be divided into several factions. Some of these factions have pursued contacts with U.S. and Canadian unions in search of support for union democracy and strategies to cope with technological change. To contact a representative of one such faction, ask for Rosario Ortíz at Mujeres en Acción Sindical.

Sindicato Mexicano de Electricistas (SME)

Antonio Caso 45
Col. San Rafael
Mailing address: A.P. 10439
México, D.F. 06470
Phone: (5) 5-35-03-86
Contact: Antonio Durán

DESCRIPTION

The SME and the Mexican Telephone Workers Union (STRM) were the two most important founding members of the Mexican Federation of Unions of Goods and Services (FESEBES) in 1990. This federation was touted by many as the forerunner of a "modernized" labor movement in Mexico, free of corruption, relatively democratic, and willing to cooperate with management and the government in the technological modernization of the country.

Consistent with this perception, the SME has maintained a progovernment and pro-NAFTA stance, but it has acted independently of the CTM in seeking contacts with U.S. and Canadian unions. The SME has advanced an "International Labor and Union Bill of Rights" to be included in NAFTA, a position similar to that taken by many U.S. and Canadian labor organizations.

In addition to taking part in trinational labor and anti-NAFTA conferences, the SME has maintained contacts with the United Electrical Workers (UE), the smallest of three electrical industry unions in the United States, since the 1970s.

Sindicato Nacional de Trabajadores de la Industria de la Costura, 19 de Septiembre

San Antonio Abad 151, Col. Obrera
Mailing address: A.P. M-10578
Col. Centro
México, D.F. 06200
Phone: (5) 7-41-33-07
Contact: Gloria Juandiego Monzón

DESCRIPTION

Formed in the aftermath of Mexico City's 1985 earthquake, the National Garment Workers Union gave top priority to publicizing the illegal labor policies of the city's hundreds of sweatshops and to halting the exodus of garment factories from the city. The government's need to regain legitimacy after its bungling of the earthquake rescue and clean-up effort allowed the September 19 union to gain official recognition—a rare accomplishment for an organization independent of government and party structures.

The union received extensive financial and organizational support from abroad, creating an international focus from the outset. Representatives have participated in many bi/trinational meetings, both on women's issues and on NAFTA.

Sindicato Nacional de Trabajadores, Obreros y Asalariados del Campo (SNTOAC)

Unidad Kennedy Edif. 276
Entrada B, Despacho 2
Col. Jardín Balbuena
México, D.F. 15900
Phone: (5) 7-68-99-73
Fax: (5) 7-64-23-49
Contact: Diego Aguilar, Secretary General

DESCRIPTION

The SNTOAC represents agricultural workers—pickers and processors—in several Mexican states. The union has between 4,000 and 5,000 members, but its contracts cover approximately 180,000 workers. It belongs to the government-affiliated Confederation of Mexican Workers (CTM). Although the CTM has been reluctant to collaborate closely with U.S. and Canadian unions, it has supported the SNTOAC's efforts to work with the Farm Labor Organizing Committee and the United Farm Workers' Union.

The SNTOAC's goals are to upgrade its labor contracts to a point where they guarantee wages and working conditions similar to those in U.S. farm-labor contracts. Toward these ends the SNTOAC and FLOC are organizing employees of agroindustrial multinationals such as Campbell Soup Co., Vlasic, and Dean's in both countries, sharing information about bargaining strategies, and offering support for strike actions.

Sindicato Unico de Trabajadores de la Secretaría de Pesca

Tabasco 303
Col. Roma
México, D.F. 06700
Phone: (5) 5-11-26-98
Fax: (5) 5-11-58-95
Contact: Alejandro Quiróz or Violeta Vázquez

LINKS

One of the largest unions affiliated with the RMALC, Sindicato Unico de Trabajadores de la Secretaría de Pesca (the Ministry of Fishing Workers Union) has established an alliance with Canada's United Fishermen and Allied Workers Union in Vancouver. In Mexico it also belongs to FESEBES.

3. UNITED STATES

Amalgamated Clothing and Textile Workers Union (ACTWU)

15 Union Square
New York, NY 10003-3377
Phone: (212) 242-0700
Contact: Ron Blackwell

DESCRIPTION

The "needle trades" unions—primarily the ACTWU and the International Ladies' Garment Workers' Union—have been perhaps the hardest hit by the shift of production out of the United States to low-wage economies. For the apparel industry this shift began long before a free trade agreement was contemplated with Mexico, and the union's response was to seek import controls to protect U.S. jobs. "[We] led the U.S. into protectionism," said one ACTWU researcher, "and now, partly because of our experience with that, we're leading the way out."

For the ACTWU this has meant a fairly cautious exploration of possible allies in Mexico, and active participation in international labor federations. In Mexico the union has quietly begun to broaden its contacts beyond the pro-NAFTA Confederation of Mexican Workers (CTM) to include the independent Authentic Labor Front (FAT). To date, the main products of these contacts have been worker education and information sharing about specific companies. "Some programmatic work" is also being undertaken—potentially involving joint campaigns targeting specific companies—but no information has been released about these activities.

A number of ACTWU offices in the Southwest have become active in cross-border issues. One is listed here.

OTHER OFFICES

ACTWU
913 S. Saint Mary
San Antonio, TX 78205
Phone: (210) 223-3223
Fax: (210) 223-9675
Contact: Glen Scott

Links

Very active in the Texas Network for Fair Trade and Clean Environment.

American Federation of Labor — Congress of Industrial Organizations (AFL - CIO)

815 16th St. NW
Washington, DC 20006
Phone: (202) 637-5187
Fax: (202) 637-5058
Contact: Ed Feigen

DESCRIPTION

As the largest labor union federation in the United States, the AFL-CIO and its forerunners have a long history of international activity, though little of it has been in Mexico. The federation has enjoyed working relations with the Confederation of Mexican Workers (CTM), and invites 10-20 CTM unionists each year to train at the George Meany Center for Labor Studies. In May 1991 the AFL-CIO signed an agreement with the CTM and the Canadian Labour Congress to protect wages in all three countries. It is not clear how this commitment is to be kept.

The AFL-CIO and the CTM set up four task forces to examine the possibility of coordinating activities in four specific industries. These task forces have been stymied by the opposing viewpoints of the two federations.

The changed international economy has opened the possibility of a broadening in the AFL-CIO's focus on supporting international capitalism to include strengthening labor movements in the third world. In Mexico this nascent shift is exemplified by the federation's decision to initiate contacts with the Authentic Labor Front (FAT), Mexico's largest independent labor organization. In part this decision was brought on by the CTM's vocal support of NAFTA, in direct opposition to the AFL-CIO's stance.

Most of the AFL-CIO's cross-border solidarity work has been initiated on a district or state level. We have listed contacts at two particularly active offices.

RESOURCES

- *Exploiting Both Sides: U.S.-Mexico "Free Trade,"* February 1991. 11 pages. $1.50.
- "The Maquiladoras and Toxics: The Hidden Costs of Production South of the Border," by Leslie Kochan, in *Safe Jobs Union Yes*, No. 186, February 1989.

OTHER OFFICES

AFL-CIO, Region VI
611 S. Shatto Place, Ste. 400
Los Angeles, CA 90005
Phone: (213) 387-1974
FAX: (213) 387-3525
Contact: Victor Muñoz

AFL-CIO, Texas
PO Box 12727
Austin, TX 78711
Phone: (512) 477-6195
Contact: Jim Cantu

American Labor Education Center (ALEC)*

2000 P St. NW #300
Washington, DC 20036
Phone: (202) 828-5170
Fax: (202) 828-5173
Email: (PeaceNet) alec

DESCRIPTION

ALEC produces educational material and videos on common interests of working people in the United States, Mexico, and Canada. It assists unionists and other activists in the three countries in making contact with one another and helps organize educational programs and solidarity actions.

ACTIVITIES

In October 1990, ALEC and the Mexican labor center SEMPO organized the conference "Common Interests."

LINKS

ALEC is a founding organizer of the U.S.-Mexico-Canada Labor Solidarity Network.

RESOURCES

- *$4 A Day? No Way!*, a 16-page illustrated summary of conditions in Mexico, free trade negotiations, and efforts to build solidarity between working people in the United States, Mexico, and Canada. $2.65 single copy; bulk rates available.
- *$4 a Day? No Way!: Joining Hands Across the Border*. Video. $30 for a VHS copy. 19 minutes.

Central America Resource Center (CARC)*

317 17th Ave. SE
Minneapolis, MN 55414-2077
Phone: (612) 627-9445
Fax: (612) 627-9450
Contact: Larry Weiss

DESCRIPTION

CARC's labor project focuses on free trade issues, particularly NAFTA.

ACTIVITIES

CARC arranges speakers for union meetings and writes articles for various publications. In 1991, it organized a trip for unionists to Mexico and Guatemala to investigate *maquiladoras* and the other side of "globalization." The group arranged for a Ford worker from Mexico to address the 1991 Minnesota AFL-CIO Convention, and for a representative of the Manitoba Federation of Labour to meet with labor groups in St. Paul and in the Iron Range region.

LINKS

The project's staff works closely with the Minnesota Fair Trade Coalition in its educational efforts.

RESOURCES

- *The Connection*. Monthly newsletter.

Communications Workers of America (CWA)*

501 3rd St. NW
Washington, DC 20001-2797
Phone: (202) 434-1185
Fax: (202) 434-1201
Contact: Steve Abrecht, Research Economist

DESCRIPTION

The CWA represents over 600,000 workers in telecommunications, government, and printing. Deregulation of the U.S. telecommunications industry presented new domestic challenges for the union in the mid-1980s. These have been compounded by increasing automation, the growth of low-wage assembly and service centers abroad, and the liberalization of the Mexican telecommunications industry.

LINKS

To respond to these changes the CWA is forging alliances with counterpart unions in Canada, Mexico, and other countries. The first of these, initiated by the Communications and Electrical Workers of Canada (CWC), is the Northern Telecom International Solidarity Coalition. This is an alliance of unions from 8 countries, including the United States and Canada—but not Mexico, where Northern Telecom has two nonunion plants—formed to pressure management at Northern Telecom to improve labor relations.

In early 1992 the CWA signed an alliance with the CWC and their Mexican counterpart, the Union of Mexican Telephone Workers (STRM). The agreement recognizes the difficulty of establishing joint positions among unions with varying political and technological positions. The three signatories committed themselves to "the permanent exchange of trade union information," and, "when necessary and possible," to "support joint mobilization."

RESOURCES

- *CWA News*.

Farm Labor Organizing Committee (FLOC)*

507 S. Saint Clair
Toledo, OH 43602
Phone: (419) 243-3456
Fax: (419) 243-5655
Contact: Baldemar Velásquez, President

DESCRIPTION

FLOC boasts nearly 25 years of experience organizing migrant farm workers in the Midwest. In 1986, prolonged negotiations with the Campbell Soup Company—supported by a national boycott of Campbell's products—produced a unique three-way agreement between FLOC, Campbell, and family farmers who grew under contract with

Campbell. During these negotiations the company threatened to move production to Mexico. In response, FLOC representatives met with counterparts in the SNTOAC, the Mexican union representing Campbell workers there.

FLOC and the SNTOAC launched the U.S.-Mexico Exchange Program at that time, and have continued to exchange information and develop bargaining strategies to work for "wage vs. living cost parity," full employment, protection of "guest workers" in the United States, and the development of "strong and democratic" unions in both countries. In 1989 FLOC's solidarity and the mobilization of its support network helped the SNTOAC win a wage increase some 15 percent higher than the government's legal cap for that year.

Fuera de Línea*

PO Box 86479
San Diego, CA 92138
Phone: (619) 291-0276
Contact: Jelger Kalmija

RESOURCES

- *Fuera de Línea* (Out of Bounds) is a quarterly, bilingual (Spanish and English) newsletter covering border topics from a working-class perspective. Particularly focusing on the development of *maquiladoras*, problems of migrant labor, the Chicano movement, and human rights, *Fuera de Línea* aims to build links among working-class organizations by providing information and resources for action. Distributed mostly in border regions. $7/yr.

Fuerza Unida*

PO Box 830083
1305 N. Flores
San Antonio, TX 78283-0083
Phone: (210) 433-2015
Contact: Viola Casares or Petra Mata

DESCRIPTION

Fuerza Unida (United Force) is an organization of 600 garment workers—the vast majority Mexican-American women—formed in January 1990. It is the product of a Levi Strauss & Co. plant closing in San Antonio that left 1,150 employees without work when the company shifted production to Costa Rica and the Dominican Republic.

ACTIVITIES

Fuerza Unida filed two lawsuits against Levi Strauss & Co., alleging pension fund violations and racial discrimination. The group also organized rallies, a boycott, and a hunger strike against the firm. A delegation attended the October 1991 trinational conference in Zacatecas, Mexico.

LINKS

Representatives have met with counterparts at La Mujer Obrera in El Paso to coordinate activities and discuss mutual problems and objectives.

International Labor Rights Education and Research Fund (ILRERF)*

PO Box 74
100 Maryland Ave. NE
Washington, DC 20002
Phone: (202) 544-7198
Fax: (202) 543-5999
Email: (PeaceNet) cdp:laborrights
Contact: Pharis Harvey

DESCRIPTION

The ILRERF is a nonprofit organization founded in 1986, representing human rights, labor, religious, consumer, academic, and business groups dedicated to assuring that workers in all countries labor under reasonable conditions, and that they are free to exercise their rights to associate, organize, and bargain collectively. The ILRERF is also committed to environmentally sound development that promotes broad-based economic growth and equitable distribution of wealth.

ACTIVITIES

The ILRERF focuses on the advancement of U.S. and international trade, investment and aid policies that promote respect for worker rights, and on field research on the status of labor rights in countries around the world, including Mexico.

The ILRERF was a leader of efforts in Washington to raise concerns about labor rights and environmental protection in the debate over NAFTA, coordinating a multi-sectorial coalition, Mobilization on Development, Trade, Labor and the Environment (MODTLE) to examine regional development in North America in conjunction with similar coalitions in Mexico and Canada.

RESOURCES

- *The Mask of Democracy: Labor Suppression in Mexico Today*, by Dan La Botz. A major study of labor rights in Mexico. (South End Press, April 1992). $14.
- *Trade's Hidden Costs: Worker Rights in a Changing World Economy.*
- *Global Village vs. Global Pillage: A One-World Strategy for Labor*, by Jeremy Brecher and Tim Costello. Advances a broad strategy for fighting the downward pull on standards that results from global competition.
- *Worker Rights News*. A newsletter on labor-rights developments.

International Ladies' Garment Workers' Union (ILGWU)

675 S. Park View St.
Los Angeles, CA 90057-3306
Phone: (213) 380-5498
Contact: Steven Nutter

OTHER OFFICES

ILGWU New York
1710 Broadway
New York, NY 10019
Phone: (212) 265-7000
Fax: (212) 489-6796
Contact: Jeff Hermanson

ILGWU El Paso
2009 Montana
El Paso, TX 79903
Phone: (915) 534-2581
Contact: John A. Herrera

International Union of Food Workers*

1875 Connecticut Ave. NW #708
Washington, DC 20009
Phone: (202) 265-4440
Fax: (202) 265-0684
Contact: Joy Ann Grune

DESCRIPTION

This group is the North American regional organization of the International Union of Food Workers, an international trade secretariat. The North American branch has eight affiliates, including the UFCW and ACTWU. Its focus is by definition international, and many of its projects are relevant to issues surrounding NAFTA.

ACTIVITIES

The union has mobilized international solidarity activities for people whose rights are violated by companies or governments, including campaigns against Nestlè and Unilever. It seeks to encourage cooperative work on strengthening international rights for women among labor, women's, and human rights groups.

LINKS

The union is a member of MODTLE.

Labor Center/Evergreen State College Labor Education Center*

Evergreen State College
Olympia, WA 98505
Phone: (206) 866-6000
Fax: (206) 866-6798
Contact: Dan Leahy, Director, or Helen Lee, Associate Director

DESCRIPTION

The Labor Center provides educational programs to labor unions throughout Washington state emphasizing history, political economy, and organizing. It works on NAFTA issues and organizes trinational educational programs with British Columbia and Mexico.

ACTIVITIES

In June 1992 the center co-sponsored a conference on "Labor and the Environment in the Global Economy," featuring union, government, and academic leaders from Canada, Mexico, and the United States. Later that month the Labor Center organized Camp Solidarity Northwest, a four-day seminar focusing on organizing strategies around free trade negotiations and the global economy.

The center held a summer seminar on the global economy in July 1991 for 225 women from the West Coast and British Columbia. Center representatives also attended the October 1991 Zacatecas Forum, and in November 1991 held a trinational conference called "Beyond Zacatecas."

Dan Leahy and Helen Lee have conducted workshops on how instructors might teach labor history in their classes, and have discussed with undergraduate students the meaning of the quincentennial for the labor movement and NAFTA.

Labor Coalition on Central America

PO Box 28014
Oakland, CA 94604
Phone: (415) 272-9951
Contact: Ben Davis

Labor Education and Research Center*

University of Oregon
1675 Agate St.
Eugene, OR 97403-1289
Phone: (503) 346-5054
Fax: (503) 346-2790
Email: claux@oregon.uoregon.edu
Contact: Steven Deutsch or Steven Hecker

DESCRIPTION

The center sponsors educational programs for working women and men, primarily in Oregon, but with some international programming.

ACTIVITIES

In September 1990 the center hosted a conference on Labor in a Global Economy, and co-hosted a sequel called Labour and the Environment in a Global Economy in June 1992, with trinational participation from Canada, the United States, and Mexico.

Labor Notes*

7435 Michigan Ave.
Detroit, MI 48210
Phone: (313) 842-6262
Fax: (313) 842-0227
Email: (PeaceNet) igc:labornotes
Contact: Mary McGinn

DESCRIPTION

Labor Notes is a national network of labor activists producing a monthly publication of news and analysis of the labor movement. It arranges classes and meetings for unionists to discuss the team concept and workplace strategies. The group also organizes tours and conferences of U.S., Mexican, and Canadian unionists in order to enhance worker-to-worker exchange and to develop strategies based on common interests.

ACTIVITIES

In November 1991, Labor Notes in conjunction with TIE organized the U.S.-Mexico-Canada Auto Workers Conference in Mexico. The conference attracted 60 auto workers from the three countries, and participants established a trinational committee of six that will coordinate information exchange and plan the next conference. Concrete plans for information exchange on individual companies, union activity, and contract negotiations were established.

LINKS

Labor Notes is one of the founding organizers of the U.S.-Mexico-Canada Labor Solidarity Network.

RESOURCES

- *Unions and Free Trade: Solidarity vs. Competition*, by Kim Moody and Mary McGinn. Includes the Canadian experience; solidarity strategies; an excellent list of readings, books, reports, studies, periodicals, documents, releases, and leaflets concerning free trade issues; and contacts in the United States, Canada, and Mexico. January 1992. $7.
- *Organizer's Packet on Free Trade*. Includes a directory of organizations in the United States, Canada, and Mexico; a step-by-step guide to starting a local union-solidarity committee; a guide to finding the employer's holdings in Mexico and to connecting with union counterparts there; advice on early detection of the employer's plans to relocate production; and photos and information on living and working conditions in Mexico. $3.
- *Labor Notes*. Monthly newsletter. $15/yr., $20 outside U.S.

Labor Studies Working Group*

Latin American Studies Association (LASA)
School of Business
Washburn University
Topeka, KS 66621
Phone: (913) 231-1010 ext. 1308
Fax: (913) 231-1063
Contact: Russell E. Smith, Associate Professor of Economics, Chair

ACTIVITIES

The Labor Studies Working Group is helping to organize and produce a special series of *Latin American Labor News* (see below) on "Labor, Free Trade, and Economic Integration in Latin America and the Caribbean." Members also present papers and participate at the Congresses of the Latin American Studies Association.

La Mujer Obrera

c/o Centro Obrero*
PO Box 3975
El Paso, TX 79923
Phone: (915) 533-9710
Contact: Angie Reynosa

DESCRIPTION

La Mujer Obrera (The Woman Laborer) is primarily an organization of Hispanic immigrant women garment workers in El Paso, Texas. Its principal objective is to organize workers to obtain genuine economic, political, and social power. It does so through programs in the areas of jobs, education, and nutrition, and through political-education work.

ACTIVITIES

Workers participate in a number of conferences and discussions regarding NAFTA and its impact on workers. La Mujer Obrera recently developed a position paper on NAFTA, based on experience in El Paso with the *maquiladora* program.

RESOURCES

- *Unidad y Fuerza*, published every two months.

Latin American Labor News*

Center for Labor Research and Studies.
University Park Campus-W MO Tr #2
Florida International University
Miami, FL 33199
Phone: (305) 348-2780
Fax: (305) 348-2241
Contact: John D. French, Editor

DESCRIPTION

Founded in 1989, *Latin American Labor News* provides up-to-date news on Latin American trade unions and their struggles, and serves as an organ for fostering intra-American labor dialogue and solidarity. Published twice a year, it also provides information on the latest research (from all scholarly disciplines) about working people in the region. The Center for Labor Research and Studies works closely with the Labor Studies Working Group of the Latin American Studies Association.

The 1992 newsletters are devoted to "Labor, Free Trade, and Economic Integration in Latin American and the Caribbean." The purpose of this series is to encourage and disseminate labor-market and labor-movement analysis of the proposed and realized trade and economic integration agreements, and to promote understanding of the kinds of cross-border linkages made by labor organizations in response to these trade initiatives.

RESOURCES

- *Latin American Labor News*. Biannually. $15/yr. individual, $30/yr. institutional.
- The Center for Labor Research and Studies also publishes a series of periodic working papers and bibliographic compilations.

Midwest Center for Labor Research

3411 Diversey Ave. #10
Chicago, IL 60647
Phone: (312) 278-5418
Fax: (312) 278-5918
Contact: Greg LeRoy

DESCRIPTION

Since its formation in 1982 as a nonprofit organization, the center has provided research and consulting assistance to labor unions, local and state governments, and community organizations. Founded by union leaders, prolabor professors, and community organizers, the center is dedicated to helping labor unions protect and improve members' standards of living and to rebuild their power as forces for justice in the workplace and economic stability in the community. The center specializes in: research useful in contract negotiations; feasibility studies and education for worker ownership; social-cost analysis; organizing against job loss and shutdowns; analysis of public subsidies; and media assistance.

RESOURCES

- *Labor Research Review*. Published twice a year. (Of special interest is No. 13, "Solidarity Across Borders: U.S. Labor in a Global Economy," Spring 1989.) $13/yr., $25/2 yrs.

National Lawyers Guild Labor and Employment Committee*

811 1st Ave. #650
Seattle, WA 98104
Phone: (206) 624-7364
Fax: (206) 624-8226
Contact: Robert H. Gibbs, Attorney-at-Law

DESCRIPTION

The committee helps build strong and democratic trade unions and assists in improving working conditions both at home and abroad.

ACTIVITIES

Its Task Force on the Free Trade Agreement coordinates the National Lawyers Guild response to NAFTA and GATT. Members took part in a May 1992 trinational conference in Mexico City on legal aspects of free trade.

LINKS

The committee is a member of MODTLE.

RESOURCES

- *Newsletter*. Distributed to members only. Five times a year. $25/yr.
- Conference report on U.S.-Mexico trade issues, by Brent Garren and Robin Alexander.

Santa Clara Center for Occupational Safety and Health (SCCOSH)*

760 N. 1st St.
San Jose, CA 95112
Phone: (408) 998-4050
Fax: (408) 998-4051
Contact: Amanda Hawes

DESCRIPTION

One of around 20 COSHs in the United States, the Santa Clara COSH specializes in trinational job health and safety training, education, and advocacy. It focuses on the needs of Latino workers, adults for whom English is a second language, and employees in high-hazard jobs, such as electronics assemblers and building-maintenance workers. The Santa Clara COSH does much of its work in the *maquiladora* industry.

LINKS

Santa Clara COSH works in coalition with other COSHs in the United States, with the Coalition for Justice in the Maquiladoras on border issues, and with the Silicon Valley Toxics Coalition.

Service Employees International Union (SEIU)

1313 L St. NW, #310
Washington, DC 20005
Phone: (202) 898-3200
Contact: Geri Palast

DESCRIPTION

Although traditionally more progressive than the older industrial unions and federations, the SEIU has taken what one activist called "a very cautious, soft-left approach" to establishing contacts in Mexico and Canada. Headquarters has neither provided much support for nor attempted to hinder its locals' efforts to create cross-border links. Four of the more active locals are listed below.

OTHER OFFICES

SEIU Local 22*
903 30th St.
Sacramento, CA 95816
Phone: (916) 441-2771
Fax: (916) 441-4596
Contact: Philip D. Reefer, President

Description

Representing workers in a diverse range of industries, Local 22 has taken a special interest in NAFTA and concerns related to fair trade, migrant workers, and seasonal workers. It is attempting to establish more contacts with independent unions, workers, and labor leaders in Mexico, to discuss issues of cross-border employment and to educate Hispanic workers regarding their legal rights in the United States as either legal or illegal temporary workers.

Resources

- *CATCH 22*. Distributed free to 4,400 workers. $5/yr. for individuals, $8/yr. for institutions.

SEIU Local 102
4004 Kearny Mesa Rd.
San Diego, CA 92111
Phone: (619) 560-0151
Contact: Elisaeo Medina

SEIU Local 790*
Fox Plaza
1390 Market St. #1118
San Francisco, CA 94102-5305
Phone: (415) 575-1740
Fax: (415) 431-6241
Contact: Frank Martín del Campo, Business Representative

Description

Local 790 has 18,000 members, representing 70 percent of city and county employees in the greater Bay Area. It is a cornerstone in the progressive labor movement in the San Francisco area, and has played a leading role in forging ties with Mexican unions.

Activities

With the backing of local central labor councils, four members joined a delegation to Mexico to meet with CTM leader Fidel Velázquez, opposition leader Cuauhtémoc Cárdenas, and officials from a wide range of unions. Out of this meeting grew an interest in the democratic movement in Mexican labor and politics. In 1992 the local will send observer teams to monitor the statewide elections in Michoacán, the site of electoral fraud in the past.

Resources

- *United Workers*. A bimonthly publication.

SEIU 1199 NW
310 W. 43 St.
New York, NY 10036
Phone: (212) 582-1890
Contact: Pat Judah Harris

Activities

Representing hospital and health care workers, this local sent a delegation to the trinational conference opposing free trade in Zacatecas, Mexico, in October 1991. It has helped organize opposition to NAFTA in New York.

Southwest Public Workers Union*

PO Box 830706
San Antonio, TX 78283
Phone/fax: (210) 299-2666
Contact: Rubén Solís or Chavel López

DESCRIPTION

From its base among public school employees, this union strives for worker and community empowerment.

ACTIVITIES

Through its labor network and via projects addressing human rights, solidarity with Mexico, and immigrant/refugee rights, the union educates people on the negative impacts of NAFTA.

RESOURCES

- *Sin Fronteras*. Quarterly. $10/yr.

Teamsters Union*

General Teamsters, Packers, Food Processors and Warehousemen's Union
25 Louisiana NW
Washington, DC 20001
Phone: (202) 624-6800
Contact: Matt Witt

OTHER OFFICES

Teamsters Union Local 912*
163 W. Lake Ave.
Watsonville, CA 95076
Phone: (408) 724-0683
Fax: (408) 724-1554
Contact: Sergio Lopez, Chavelo Moreno, or Joe Fahey

Activities

Local 912 union representatives have traveled to Mexico, Canada, and across the United States publicizing Pillsbury/Green Giant's firing of almost 400 long-term Watsonville workers (see Trabajadores Desplazados). The union campaign also examines the links between transnational corporations like Pillsbury's owner, Grand Metropolitan, and hunger and pollution in Mexico. Local 912, in conjunction with Mexican workers, continues to pressure Green Giant to pay its Mexican workers a decent wage and to build a treatment plant for the wastewater it and its growers use to irrigate crops.

Joining with environmental groups, Local 912 informs consumers about Mexico's lack of pesticide regulations, and helped win a court ruling against the U.S. Customs Service to enforce 'country of origin' labeling on imported vegetables.

Resources

- *Dirty Business, Food Exports to the United States*. Initiated by the Teamsters, this video has been the subject of numerous local, regional, and national stories. (Migrant Media Productions, PO Box 2048, Freedom, CA 95019. [408] 728-8949). 1/2 in. VHS. 15 minutes. $35 postpaid for labor and grassroots organizations.

Tennessee Industrial Renewal Network (TIRN)

1515 E. Magnolia Ave. #408
Knoxville, TN 37917
Phone: (615) 637-1576
Contact: Bill Troy

DESCRIPTION

Co-sponsored by TIRN's Maquiladora Project and ACTWU, two *maquiladora* workers held a public meeting in Knoxville, Tennessee, in February 1991. Their visit included trips to union halls, factories, restaurants, landfills, and offices to meet the working people of Tennessee. These women are members of the Comité Fronterizo de Obreras based in Matamoros and Reynosa, Mexico, a group that organizes around the legal rights of *maquiladora* workers.

Trabajadores Desplazados*

434 Main St. #222
Watsonville, CA 95076
Phone: (408) 728-5671
Fax: (408) 728-5671
Contact: Mike Kostyal

DESCRIPTION

Trabajadores Desplazados (Displaced Workers) is a committee of workers laid off by Green Giant in Watsonville, California. Most are middle-age Mexican women, immigrants who had been employed by Green Giant for an average of 14 years. Since April 1991 the group has maintained a boycott of Green Giant and its parent companies—Pillsbury and Grand Metropolitan—to protest the layoffs, the starvation wages paid by the company at its new plant in Mexico, and the company's use of badly polluted water for irrigation. The workers engage in a solidarity project with Gigante Verde workers in Irapuato, Mexico, and participate in activities to achieve a fair trade agreement.

LINKS

The group works closely with Teamsters Union Local 912.

Transnationals Information Exchange (TIE)*

7435 Michigan Ave.
Detroit, MI 48210
Phone: (313) 842-6262
Fax: (313) 842-0227
Email: (PeaceNet) igc:labornotes
Contact: Mary McGinn

DESCRIPTION

TIE, an organization based in Amsterdam, is funded by unions and charitable foundations. It has helped union members to build international networks in auto, cocoa/chocolate production, and telecommunications.

ACTIVITIES

In November 1991, TIE, in conjunction with Labor Notes, organized the U.S.-Mexico-Canada Auto Workers Conference in Mexico. The conference attracted 60 auto workers from the three countries, and participants established a trinational committee of six that will coordinate information exchange and plan the next conference. Concrete plans for information exchange on individual companies, union activity, and contract negotiations were established.

Tri-National Commission for Justice in the Maquiladoras*

10706 Anderson Ct.
Sugar Creek, MO 64054
Phone: (816) 836-3242
Fax: (816) 454-6341
Contact: Jack Hedrick, Coordinator

DESCRIPTION

The commission focuses on research into the long-range effects of free trade and *maquiladoras* on the lives of the working class in the United States, Canada, and Mexico. It encourages public education about ways to improve working conditions and to promote social and economic growth. The coordinator, Jack Hedrick, is active with UAW Local 249 in Liberty, Missouri. He has traveled to Mexico to support the Ford Workers Democratic Movement.

LINKS

The commission is a member of the Fair Trade Campaign, the National Toxics Campaign, the Federation for Industrial Retention and Renewal, and the Coalition for Justice in the Maquiladoras.

RESOURCES

- *Trade Watch*. Biweekly. Free.

Unión de Trabajadores Agrícolas Fronterizos (UTAF)*

514 S. Kansas
El Paso, TX 79901
Phone: (915) 532-0921
Fax: (915) 532-0924
Contact: Carlos Marentes, Director

ACTIVITIES

UTAF attempts to improve wages and working conditions of agricultural workers living along the U.S.-Mexico border. Its current priority is organizing in the chile fields of southern New Mexico.

The union also conducts educational activities directed to *ejidatarios* (small, communal farmers) who work in U.S. agriculture, and has participated in the General Assembly of Border Agricultural Workers and in labor stoppages during the chile harvest.

LINKS

UTAF has a working relationship with human rights groups from Mexico, including the Frente Democrático Campesino from the state of Chihuahua.

RESOURCES

- *El Bote Sin Copete*. Every two months plus special editions during the growing season. 25¢ suggested donation.

United Automobile, Aerospace, Agricultural Implement Workers of America (UAW)*

1757 N St. NW
Washington, DC 20036
Phone: (202) 828-8500
Fax: (202) 293-3457
Contact: Steve Beckman, International Economist

ACTIVITIES

In early 1992 the UAW responded to the arrest of the leader of the Union of Day Laborers in Matamoros by sending a letter of protest to the Mexican government, and a check for $15,000 to the union. But the UAW's international solidarity work occurs primarily through the International Metalworkers Federation. The federation has not yet taken a position on NAFTA, but is planning a conference on North American integration in December 1992.

LINKS

Although roughly 75,000 Mexicans work for U.S.-owned automakers or their suppliers, the UAW has made relatively little effort to establish links with Mexican labor organizations. One obstacle is the lack of a national auto workers union in Mexico; most auto-related plants have local unions affiliated directly with the Confederation of Mexican Workers (CTM) or other confederations. A second is the opposing positions on NAFTA taken by the CTM and the UAW, leaving little common ground on which to build a foundation of cooperation, according to one UAW official. Indicative of this problem was the fate of the automobile industry task force set up by the AFL-CIO and the CTM. The task force fizzled after one meeting in 1990, when it became clear that "we didn't agree on much of anything."

Probably the most important obstacle to collaboration, however, is the UAW's wish to avoid the appearance of interfering in the internal affairs of Mexican unions. Working with dissident factions that would be more receptive to the UAW's perspective—as a few UAW locals have done—runs the risk of angering the official Mexican unions and potentially inviting retribution.

OTHER OFFICES

UAW Local 879*
MEXUSCAN Solidarity Task Force
2191 Ford Parkway
St. Paul, MN 55116
Phone: (612) 699-4246
Fax: (612) 699-3876
Email: (PeaceNet) igc:tlaney
Contact: Tom Laney, Recording Secretary

Description

This is probably the most active UAW local in the country in terms of building ties with Mexican workers. As small-truck assemblers for Ford, members of the local were inspired to establish the MEXUSCAN Solidarity Task Force by the repression of Ford workers in Cuautitlán, Mexico, in early 1990.

Activities

The task force has divided its attention between local education and coalition-building efforts and international networking. Representatives attended a trinational anti-

NAFTA conference in October 1990, and a trinational auto workers conference in November 1991. In January 1991, the local co-sponsored a conference on solidarity vs. competition, with a presentation by two members of the Mexican Ford Workers Democratic Movement. This conference led to the formation of the Minnesota Fair Trade Coalition.

The local leadership faces opposition from members who believe that resources should be concentrated on local activities rather than international solidarity. One of its objectives is therefore to acquaint enough members of the local with the Mexican investment situation to keep the solidarity work politically viable.

Links

MODTLE; UAW/New Directions Movement; Minnesota Fair Trade Coalition; Labor Notes; Central America Resource Center; and to the extent possible, the Democratic Farmer Labor Party and trades groups. Sponsors exchanges with Mexican Ford workers.

Resources

- *Step-by-Step*. A chronological description of the work Local 879 did to form the trinational MEXUSCAN Solidarity Task Force with active support from its membership.
- *The Local 879 Autoworker*. Monthly newsletter for the local. Free to interested parties.

UAW/New Directions Movement

PO Box 6876
St. Louis, MO 63144
Phone: (314) 531-2900
Contact: Jerry Tucker

Description

A dissident movement within the UAW seeking to reform the union's leadership-selection procedure and to abolish its "jointness" program, which stresses cooperation with employers over more adversarial relations. Many New Directions Movement activists urge the pursuit of links with independent or dissident Mexican labor movements.

United Electrical, Radio, and Machine Workers of America (UE)*

1800 Diagonal Rd. #600
Alexandria, VA 22314
Phone: (703) 684-3123 Washington Office/(412) 471-8919 National Office
Contacts: Bob Kingsley, Political Director (Washington), or Amy Newell, Secretary-Treasurer (National Office)

DESCRIPTION

The UE is the smallest and most progressive of the three major U.S. unions representing workers in electrical industries.

LINKS

In March 1992 the UE signed a "Strategic Organizing Alliance" with the Authentic Labor Front (FAT) of Mexico. The alliance is potentially very significant, as it facilitates joint actions or bargaining with individual corporations. Neither the FAT nor the UE, however, have revealed their plans for the alliance, apart from increased communication and cooperation. The alliance appears to represent the closest coordination yet between the leadership of a major U.S. union and an independent Mexican union. Dave Johnson is the UE's primary representative with the FAT.

The UE has also worked with the Mexican Electricians Union (SME) and the now-defunct Nuclear Workers Union (SUTIN), largely on exchanges of information and perspectives. Humberto Camacho in the Compton office (see below) is the UE's contact person for dealings with the SME.

We have included addresses and contacts for several UE district or local offices that have been active in building cross-border links.

OTHER OFFICES

UE National Organizing Office
828 N. Bristol St. #101
Santa Ana, CA 92703
Phone: (714) 836-4101
Contact: Dave Johnson

UE District 1
4343 Kelly Dr.
Philadelphia, PA 19129
Phone: (215) 438-0800
Contact: Bob Brown

UE
37 S. Ashland
Chicago, IL 60607
Phone: (312) 277-0204
Contact: Lydia Sanchez

UE Local 1421
14819 Atlantic Ave
Compton, CA 90221
Phone: (310) 638-7881
Contact: Humberto Camacho

Links

With support from the national leadership, Local 1421 has taken the lead in establishing contacts with the Mexican Electricians Union (SME). These contacts, begun in the early 1970s, have grown since the announcement of NAFTA talks. In June 1992, UE representatives from the United States and Canada along with officials of the Canadian Auto Workers union (CAW) met at the SME office in Mexico to continue discussions on a joint position vis-à-vis NAFTA and the *maquiladoras*. A major obstacle, however, is the pro-NAFTA position of the SME. One optimistic activist felt that this position may move closer to the UE's, noting "the seeds are there now." Local 1421 has also taken an active interest in environmental issues, supporting efforts in Tijuana to ban the construction of a U.S.-owned waste incinerator there.

United Food and Commercial Workers

1775 K St. NW
Washington, DC 20006
Phone: (202) 466-1560
Fax: (202) 466-1562
Contact: Segundo Mercado

United Steelworkers of America

815 16th St. NW
Washington, DC 20006
Phone: (202) 638-6929
Contact: Jack Sheehan

PART III

Environment

INTRODUCTION

Environmental activism around trade issues is a recent phenomenon on the North American continent. In the past several years national and local environmental groups in Canada, the United States, and Mexico have begun insisting that international trade accords include environmental standards. Most of this attention is focused on the NAFTA negotiations but environmental groups, particularly the national U.S. organizations, are also active in promoting environmental standards in the GATT negotiations through the United Nations and with multilateral lending institutions. The NAFTA negotiations have spawned a flurry of cross-border links among environmental organizations and have spurred environmental organizations to join in coalitions with unions, consumer groups, and social justice activists.

In Canada, the main concern of environmental groups has been that regulatory standards are usually harmonized downward in free trade agreements, thereby threatening their country's often stricter environmental standards and leading to increased environmental deterioration through higher concentration of acid rain and the continuing depletion of the ozone layer. The initiation of NAFTA negotiations forced U.S. environmental organizations to begin to seriously address international trade and economic issues. In Mexico, the dumping of hazardous wastes and contamination from the *maquiladora* industry are of major concern to the fledgling environmental movement. Thus national and border-area groups in Mexico are struggling for a NAFTA accord with increased environmental regulation and higher standards. However, the dissolution of SEDUE and the absorption of its functions into the Secretaría de Desarrollo Social (SEDESOL) will have untold effects on the quality of Mexico's environmental enforcement efforts and on the character and efficacy of binational environmental-protection activities. At the same time, many U.S. environmental and conservation organizations are critical of the U.S. government's Environmental Protection Agency for its lax enforcement of domestic environmental protection regulations and for inadequately addressing factors in Mexico that threaten the environment and would likely be exacerbated under NAFTA.

Before the NAFTA negotiations began there were few cross-border environmental links, but in the process of reviewing the proposed free trade agreement many groups increased monitoring of the environmental impact of foreign investment. Before NAFTA the only U.S. groups active in Mexico were conservation organizations such as the Audubon Society and the National Wildlife Federation, which sponsored reserves and wildlife-preservation projects in Mexico. Increasingly, national-level U.S. organizations are interacting with Mexico City-based groups, though few links yet exist within Mexico between northern border organizations and the Mexico City groups.

1. CANADA

Canadian Environmental Law Association*

517 College St. #401
Toronto, ON M6G 4A2
Phone: (416) 960-2284
Fax: (416) 960-9392
Contact: Michelle Swenarchuk, Acting Director

DESCRIPTION

The Canadian Environmental Law Association is a world leader in researching the environmental implications of free trade. It provides free legal services to environmental groups and individuals affected by environmental problems, and is involved in research, political action, and publicizing the environmental effects of trade. It maintains a library with legal and scientific materials related to the environment.

RESOURCES

- *Newsletter*. Bimonthly. $18/yr.
- *Environmental Impacts of the Canada-U.S. Free Trade Agreement*, by Michelle Swenarchuk. February 1988.
- *Free Trading the Environment*, by Frank James Tester, in the *Free Trade Deal* edited by Duncan Cameron, James Lorimer and Company, Toronto, 1988.
- *Implications of the Free Trade Agreement for Canadian Electricity Exports*, by Ian Blue. *Free Trade And the Provinces*, by Andrew Petter. Two papers presented at the National Conference on the Free Trade Agreement, Osgoode Hall Law School. March 1988.
- *Selling Canada's Environment Short: The Environmental Case Against The Trade Deal*, by Steven Shrybman, Counsel to the Canadian Environmental Law Association. Analysis endorsed by Friends of the Earth (Canada) and the Movement pour L'Agriculture Biologique. $1.
- *The Canada-U.S. Free Trade Agreement*. Canada, 1987 (with explanatory text and tariff schedules).
- *The Impact of the Canada/U.S. Trade Agreement: A Legal Analysis*, by the Attorney General for Ontario. May 1988.
- *Under the Label of "Free Trade" Canada is Being Asked to Support an Unprecedented Surrender of Our Resources*, by Ian McDougall, in *If You Love This Country*, assembled by Laurier Lapierre. M & S, 1988.
- *Water and the Canada-United States Free Trade Agreement: A Summary Assessment*. Prepared by the Rawson Academy of Aquatic Science. Ottawa, July 29, 1988.

Canadian Environmental Network

251 Laurier Ave. W. #1004
Ottawa, ON K1P 5J6
Phone: (613) 563-2078
Fax: (613) 563-7326

DESCRIPTION

The Canadian Environmental Network is an umbrella organization linking the majority of Canadian environmental groups at the local, state, and national level.

RESOURCES

- *Green List.* Book that describes more than 400 Canadian environmental organizations.

Cultural Survival

1 Nicholas St. #420
Ottawa, ON K1N 7B7
Phone: (613) 233-4653
Fax: (613) 233-2292
Contact: Heather Hamilton, National Coordinator

DESCRIPTION

Founded in 1972, Cultural Survival has taken a position against NAFTA.

Friends of the Earth

251 Laurier Ave. #701
Ottawa, ON K1P 5J6
Phone: (613) 230-3352
Fax: (613) 232-4354
Contact: Susan Tanner

ACTIVITIES

As part of an international organization, Friends of the Earth focuses on climate change, protection of the ozone layer, and the global warming implications of NAFTA. It does advocacy work and briefs parliamentarians.

Pollution Probe

12 Madison Ave.
Toronto, ON M5R 2S1
Phone: (416) 926-1907
Fax: (416) 926-1601
Contact: Jeanine Ferretti, Executive Director

LINKS

Pollution Probe collaborates with the National Wildlife Federation.

Sierra Club Canada

1 Nicholas St. #420
Ottawa, ON K1N 7B7
Phone: (613) 233-1906
Fax: (613) 233-2292
Contact: Elizabeth May

DESCRIPTION

Sierra Club Canada is publicly active in its opposition to NAFTA.

LINKS

Though affiliated with the U.S. Sierra Club, the group has a separate identity and board.

Consejo de Salud del Noreste de Sonora y Condado Cochise

Centro de Salud
Calle 4, Av. 10
Agua Prieta, Son.
Phone: (633) 8-15-63
Contact: Héctor Carrillo

DESCRIPTION

Consejo de Salud, the Health Council for Northeast Sonora (Mexico) and Cochise County (United States), formerly Comité Binacional de Salud Douglas-Agua Prieta, adopts an interdisciplinary approach to environmental issues, incorporating attorneys, scientists, and technicians within its staff.

ACTIVITIES

It has recently begun to research and present testimony about the potential impacts of NAFTA.

LINKS

It has cooperated with such groups as the Community Nutrition Institute, Environmental Defense Fund, Public Citizen, and Texas Center for Policy Studies in presenting testimony and comments on NAFTA. It is also building links with such Mexico City-based organizations as Grupo de los Cien.

Enlace Ecológico (EECO)*

Calle 16, Av. 16 #1598
Agua Prieta, Son. 84200
Phone: (633) 8-06-76/8-37-13
Fax: (633) 4-01-28
U.S. mailing address: PO Box 186, Douglas, AZ 85608
Contact: Gildardo Acosta Ruíz or Miguel Angel González

DESCRIPTION

Enlace Ecológico (Ecological Link) studies environmental problems in the Sonoran border region by serving as a mediator between nongovernmental organizations and government offices of both countries.

ACTIVITIES

Enlace Ecológico is an active promoter and coordinator of the nongovernmental network Red de Salud y Medio Ambiente (see p. 77) and of Consejo de Salud del Noreste. Its speakers have participated in the EPA/SEDUE public hearings to discuss the effects of NAFTA on the border environment. In addition, Enlace Ecológico developed a draft Local Emergency Response Plan, and in conjunction with the Border Ecology Project developed the first Hazardous Materials Inventory in the Douglas-Agua Prieta area.

LINKS

Enlace Ecológico is the Mexican counterpart of Arizona Toxics Information and the Border Ecology Project.

Foro Ecologista de Baja California*

Avenida de las Palmas 317
Fraccionamiento Palmas
Tijuana, B.C. 22200
Phone: (66) 81-21-42
Fax: (66) 81-21-42
Contact: Jorge A. Caldera Pérez

DESCRIPTION

This group of professionals opposes environmental contamination in Baja California, principally in Tijuana, Mexicali, Tecate, and Ensenada.

ACTIVITIES

Together with Greenpeace and the Environmental Health Coalition, Foro Ecologista (Ecological Forum) tries to monitor the work of Chemical Waste Management company. They also promote open forums with representatives from both pesticide companies and affected communities.

Foro Mexicano de la Sociedad Civil/Río 92*
— defunct (see Addendum)

Allende 7
Col. Sta. Ursula Coapa
México, D.F. 04650
Phone: (5) 6-84-02-53/03-77
Contact: Julio Romaní

DESCRIPTION

Foro Mexicano (Mexican Forum) is an association of individuals, environmental movements, indigenous groups, and nongovernmental organizations (NGOs) that research and analyze ecological and social development issues. The forum supports a regulated economy based on the necessity for cooperation and social justice, without exploitation of the natural environment. It proposes banning the import/export of contaminating or toxic industrial products, passage of international laws regulating the conduct of transnational corporations, and the imposition of sanctions on any commercial exchange that contributes to environmental deterioration or abuses cheap labor to augment profit.

ACTIVITIES

The forum has participated in international NGO conferences in Geneva and Río de Janeiro parallel to United Nations conferences on the environment.

LINKS

The forum maintains links with RMALC and with ecological groups from Mexico City, Morelos, Jalisco, Oaxaca, Michoacán, Veracrúz, and Quintana Roo.

Grupo de los Cien Artistas e Intelectuales

Sierra Jiutepec 155-B
Col. Lomas Barrilaco
México, D.F. 11010
Phone: (5) 5-40-73-79
Fax: (5) 5-20-35-77
Contact: Homero Aridjis

ACTIVITIES

Jointly with the U.S.-based Alert Citizens for Environmental Safety, the Mexico City-based Grupo de los Cien opposes plans by the Texas state government to locate a nuclear waste dump near the small town of Sierra Blanca in Hudspeth County, southeast of El Paso, Texas. The site is only 20 miles from the Mexican border.

LINKS

The Grupo de los Cien and Alert Citizens for Environmental Safety (ACES) are committed to the long-term preservation of the border and its natural resources. Grupo de los Cien also works with the National Wildlife Federation.

Pacto de Grupos Ecologistas (PGE)

Explanada 705
Col. Lomas de Chapultepec
México, D.F. 11000
Contact: Ignacio Peón Escalante

DESCRIPTION

Pacto de Grupos Ecologistas (the Pact of Environmental Groups) comprises over 70 social-movement organizations around the nation working to defend the environment. The PGE engages in research projects, social-development activities, and information exchanges with communities, local peasant organizations, and government agencies.

LINKS

The Pacto de Grupos Ecologistas is a member of RMALC and has links with The Other Economic Summit and the National Wildlife Federation.

Proyecto Fronterizo de Educación Ambiental

Calle Lava 27
Sección Jardines
Tijuana, B.C.
Phone: (66) 30-05-90
Contact: Laura Durazo

ACTIVITIES

In Baja California and along the southern California border, Proyecto Fronterizo de Educación Ambiental (the Border Project for Environmental Education) is engaged in a program of public education through meetings with working-class neighborhoods, industry, fire departments, and citizens groups, using audio-visual educational tools. Working with the Border Ecology Project, Proyecto Fronterizo created a directory of border organizations and individuals concerned with transboundary environmental problem solving. The directory is accompanied by an ongoing database maintained jointly by the two groups.

Red de Acción sobre Plaguicidas y Alternativas en México (RAPAM)*

Vesubio 57
Col. Alpes
México, D.F. 01010
Phone: (5) 5-93-76-59
Fax: (5) 6-89-76-09
Contact: Fernando Bejarano or María Eugenia Acosta

DESCRIPTION

As the Mexican office of the Pesticide Action Network, RAPAM researches the issue of harmonization of consumer-protection standards within NAFTA, and promotes information exchange regarding illegal pesticides. RAPAM sponsors prevention workshops dealing with the risks of using pesticides and provides alternatives in biological control of plagues.

RESOURCES

- *Boletín de la RAPAM* (RAPAM Bulletin). Quarterly. Information about problems caused by the abuse of chemical pesticides as well as ecologically sound agricultural alternatives.

3. UNITED STATES

Alert Citizens for Environmental Safety (ACES)*

519 1/2 Prospect St.
El Paso, TX 79902
Phone: (915) 534-7350
Fax: (915) 590-8088
Contact: Linda Lynch, President

DESCRIPTION

ACES is a nonprofit organization formed in 1983. Through research, education, and activism, ACES promotes the long-term protection of West Texas' and the U.S./Mexico border region's natural resources, especially in the West Texas/Trans-Pecos region. ACES provides information to the communities in Hudspeth County in far West Texas that would be affected by the construction of a nuclear-waste dump in the county.

ACTIVITIES

Jointly with the Mexican Grupo de los Cien, ACES opposes plans by the Texas state government to locate a nuclear waste dump near the small town of Sierra Blanca in Hudspeth County, southeast of El Paso, Texas. The site is only 20 miles from the Mexican border. The group is also active in monitoring other hazardous-waste dumping in this border area.

LINKS

Works in cooperation with Grupo de los Cien.

Appropriate Technology Working Group/Appropriate Development Exchange (AT-Work/ADE)*

Earth Island Institute
300 Broadway #28
San Francisco, CA 94133-3312
Phone: (415) 788-3666
Fax: (415) 788-7324
Email: (EcoNet) earthisland
Contact: Robert Frey

DESCRIPTION

AT-Work/ADE is part of the Earth Island Institute, a nonprofit organization working with labor, material aid, and fundraising to develop innovative projects for the conservation, preservation, and restoration of the global environment. AT-Work/ADE organizes groups of volunteers to assist sustainable technology projects around the world.

ACTIVITIES

Emerging AT-Work efforts include a U.S.-Mexico Border Project addressing toxic disasters in *maquiladora* areas along the border. The group also sponsors seminars, tours, receptions, lectures, and an annual concert.

LINKS

It has established contact with an independent group advocating for the rights of native inhabitants of the largest remaining rainforest in Mexico—the Chimalapas region.

Arizona Toxics Information*

PO Box 1896
Bisbee, AZ 85603
Phone: (602) 432-7340
Fax: (602) 432-7340
Contact: Michael Gregory, Director

DESCRIPTION

This advocacy and policy-development organization provides information on toxic substances—including prevention, control, hazards, and regulatory/statutory action. It has been intimately involved with development of the La Paz Agreement, NAFTA, and the EPA/SEDUE Integrated Border Environmental Plan (IBEP).

ACTIVITIES

In August and September 1991, Arizona Toxics Information, Enlace Ecológico, and the Border Ecology Project sponsored two public forums in Douglas, Arizona, and Agua Prieta, Sonora, to inform area residents about EPA/SEDUE's Integrated Border Environmental Plan and to prepare testimony for the EPA/SEDUE hearings. The forums were attended by 60-80 participants, most of them from Mexico. They represented a cross-section of the area communities, drawing from Bisbee, Cananea, Douglas, Nacozari, Esqueda, Naco, Sierra Vista, and Tucson. Officials from city and county governments, as well as representatives of SEDUE, attended. The groups represented a wide variety of occupations, including health, agriculture, mining, utilities, and emergency planning. Participants identified more than 150 specific environmental issues to be addressed in the IBEP, as well as a number of strategies and goals for plan implementation. Many participants addressed procedural issues, including the structure of the plan itself and the process by which it is being developed.

RESOURCES

- *Findings of Public Forums on EPA/SEDUE Integrated Border Environmental Plan.*
- *Sustainable Development vs. Economic Growth: Environmental Protection as an Investment in the Future*. Statement of Michael Gregory before the International Trade Commission Hearing on Probable Economic Effect on U.S. Industries and Consumers of a Free Trade Agreement between the United States and Mexico held at Scottsdale, Arizona, April 1991.
- *Testimony of Michael Gregory before the U.S. Trade Representative Hearing on the North American Free Trade Agreement* held at San Diego, California, August 1991.
- *Transparency, Local Control and Binational Cooperation: Adding Conditions of Sustainability to the proposed North American Free Trade Agreement*. Presented by Michael Gregory in Guadalajara during the national meeting: El Tratado de Libre Comercio y las Universidades Mexicanas, November 1991.
- *U.S.-Mexico Free Trade Negotiations and the Environment, Exploring the Issues*, By Mary E. Kelly (Texas Center for Policy Studies), Dick Kamp (Border Ecology Project), Jan Rich, and Michael Gregory. Published by The Columbia Journal of World Business, Summer 1991.

Border Ecology Project (BEP)*

PO Drawer CP
Bisbee, AZ 85603
Phone: (602) 432-7456
Fax: (602) 432-7473
Contact: Dick Kamp or Geoffrey Land

DESCRIPTION

The Border Ecology Project is one of the most active private, nonprofit environmental groups along the U.S.-Mexico border. Its staff and board consist of residents of both countries concerned with environmental issues as part of a broader social reality in the border region. BEP has been involved in issues affecting other areas of North America as an outgrowth of successful problem resolution in the Arizona-Sonora area. Examples include an examination of U.S. foreign policy and air pollution impacts on Canada, and planning for nationwide labor impacts of U.S. air pollution control. Both areas of research grew from development of border-area copper-smelter pollution control.

ACTIVITIES

BEP was the main force behind the creation and implementation of a 1987 U.S.-Mexico treaty regulating air pollution from all smelters located within 100 kilometers of the border. They were active in the drafting of a 1987 transboundary hazardous-material control agreement, signed by both countries to regulate international movement of hazardous waste and materials. During the early 1990s, BEP collaborated with the University of Arizona Udall Center, Colegio de la Frontera Norte, Instituto Tecnológico de Sonora, and various government agencies in a project on Sonora, Arizona, to assess water quality and supply and to create binational, water-management recommendations. The joint study uncovered solvent contamination in the Nogales aquifer.

LINKS

In 1990, BEP began a border health and environmental networking and outreach project (La Red) based in Baja California and San Diego designed to increase communications between concerned individuals and groups in the border region. Members are drawn from the Mexican organizations Enlace Ecológico, Colegio de Sonora, Grupo Ecológico los Campitos (Cananea, Sonora), Grupo Dignidad (Nogales, Sonora), Colegio de la Frontera Norte, Proyecto Fronterizo de Educación Ambiental; and from the U.S. groups Southern Arizona Environment Management Society, and Udall Center for Studies in Public Policy.

RESOURCES

- *Directory of Ecology in the Border region.*
- *Capsule Summaries of Selected U.S.-Mexico Environmental Problems and Strategies*, by Dick Kamp. Document presented to the Congressional Study Group on Mexico/Session on U.S.-Mexico Ecology: Respecting No Frontier. October 1989.
- *Nogales: Industrialization, Water Pollution and Policy Options*, by Dick Kamp. November 1990.
- *Maquilas and Hazardous Materials: Some Arizona-Sonora Experiences*, by Dick Kamp.

Border Progress Foundation/Fundación Progreso Fronterizo*

PO Box 70164
San Diego, CA 92167
Phone: (619) 453-0352
Fax: (619) 453-2165
Contact: Elsa R. Saxod or Gail Sevrens

DESCRIPTION

The Border Progress Foundation attempts to mobilize community-service and self-help projects to meet environmental and social-infrastructure needs along the Mexico-U.S. border. Patterned on the Bush administration's "Thousand Points of Light" initiative and influenced by EPA and SEDUE efforts on the Integrated Environmental Border Plan, the foundation acts as a catalyst in promoting volunteerism, self-help, and community-betterment programs along the border. Border Progress is being established as a nonprofit charitable organization in the United States, and also in Mexico. Progreso Fronterizo serves as Border Progress' liaison for projects undertaken on the Mexican side of the border. Among Border Progress' key objectives is to persuade U.S. and foreign corporations with *maquiladora* and twin-plant facilities to become more active in their host border communities through financial assistance, in-kind donations, and the promotion of community-service projects and activities.

ACTIVITIES

The foundation encourages community-endowment funds and facilitates fundraising for projects undertaken by nonprofit organizations in border towns. "Funding facilitation" assistance areas include: community development, health, housing, and education (including environmental education). The possibility of Border Progress being the promoter of a U.S.-Mexico Border Youth Conservation Corps is also being examined. Border Progress aims to facilitate increased corporate giving and philanthropy in the U.S.-Mexico border region through a four-step process including: a) promoting corporate awareness; b) project identification and screening; c) corporate participation; d) establishment of endowment funds for sister-cities in regions lacking the support of a community foundation (e.g. Calexico, Nogales, Douglas, Southern New Mexico, Eagle Pass, Laredo, McAllen, Brownsville).

LINKS

The Border Progress Foundation is closely associated with SEDUE and EPA. It also seeks to establish links with the Business Roundtable, the U.S. Council for International Business, the National Foreign Trade Council, the Mexico-U.S. Business Committee (U.S. section), Consejo Nacional de la Industria Maquiladora, the Border Trade Alliance, and other trade associations.

RESOURCES

- *Border Progress*. Bimonthly newsletter aimed at identifying projects and nonprofit organizations working to make a difference along the U.S.-Mexican border. Each issue includes an updated inventory of recommended projects for possible funding.

Citizens' Environmental Coalition (CEC)*

33 Central Ave.
Albany, NY 12210
Phone: (518) 462-5527
Contact: David Aube

DESCRIPTION

CEC is a statewide coalition of 80 community, environmental, and labor groups working on toxic waste and other pollution problems in New York State. CEC provides citizen assistance, information, and referral regarding the technical, health, governmental, and organizing aspects of pollution problems. CEC advocates statewide policy reforms on hazardous, pesticide, industrial, and radioactive waste.

ACTIVITIES

CEC was a key organizer of the November 1991 Third Annual Labor & Environment Conference in Albany planned by a broad-based coalition of 31 organizations in New York State, including AFL-CIO (NY), UAW 686, and the International Brotherhood of Electrical Workers 2213. "Labor, the Environment and Free Trade" is one of the 8 priority focuses of the Conference's Plan of Action for 1992.

RESOURCES

- *Toxics In Your Community*. Quarterly newsletter. $15/yr. Spring 1991 and Winter 1992 newsletters include articles about free trade.
- *A Directory of State & National Organizations: Building a Movement for Labor & Environmental Justice*, by Jamie Gilkey & Anne Rabe, Director, CEC. More than 75 organizations listed. 1990. $3.
- Reports and citizen guides on toxic waste, air pollution, hazardous waste technologies, toxic measurements, and campaign contributions by polluters.

Community Nutrition Institute (CNI)*

2001 S St. NW #530
Washington, DC 20009
Phone: (202) 462-4700
Fax: (202) 462-5241
Contact: Rodney Leonard, Executive Director, or John Morrill, Government Relations/Trade Director

DESCRIPTION

CNI is a nonprofit, consumer-interest group advocating programs and services that enable Americans to enjoy a safer and healthier diet. The group supports measures to ensure that poor people have access to food, and to encourage Americans to follow healthy dietary practices. It also addresses free trade, border ecology, and agriculture issues.

RESOURCES

- *The North American Free Trade Agreement (NAFTA): Opening the Door to Environmental Disaster?*, by Eric Christensen and Rodney Leonard for the Community Nutrition Institute. Fall 1991. 36 pages. $4.50.

- *Testimony of Rodney Leonard and Eric Christensen of Behalf of the Community Nutrition Institute on the Economic Effects of a Free Trade Agreement between Mexico and the U.S.* April 1991. 26 pages. $3.50.
- *CNI Brief Concerning Negotiation of a North American Free Trade Agreement*, by Eric Christensen and Rodney Leonard. August 1991. 25 pages. $3.50.

Ecological Life Systems Institute (ELSI)*

2923 E. Spruce St.
San Diego, CA 92104
Phone: (619) 281-1447
Contact: Jim Bell, Director

DESCRIPTION

ELSI is a nonprofit organization that provides lectures, consultation, and technical services on environmentally sensitive designs for residential, commercial, and industrial applications. Its work focuses on involving people in the learning process of discovering how to live and make a living on this planet in ways that are ecologically sustainable and fair to everyone involved.

ACTIVITIES

Jim Bell is Project Director for the Wastewater Treatment and Recycling Project, SIDETRAN, in Tijuana (COLEF), and delivers lectures on both sides of the border on how to make the Tijuana/San Diego region ecologically sustainable. The group's mapping project, based on watersheds, links the Tijuana/San Diego region as one planning area.

LINKS

ELSI participates as a member of the binational Environmental Committee of the Tijuana/San Diego Region.

Environmental Committee of the Tijuana-San Diego Region*

U.N. Building
Balboa Park
San Diego, CA 92101
Phone: (66) 86-36-87 (Tijuana); (619) 285-9432/531-6485 (San Diego)
Fax: (619) 531-5199
Contact: José Luis Morales (Tijuana) or Kaare S. Kjos (San Diego)

DESCRIPTION

The Environmental Committee of the Tijuana-San Diego Region is an alliance of environmentally oriented groups and individuals from both sides of the U.S.-Mexico border. It is a demonstration project of the United Nations Association of San Diego County created to maintain a binational network promoting sustainable development through educational programs.

Environmental Defense Fund (EDF)*

257 Park Ave. S.
New York, NY 10010
Phone: (212) 505-2100
Fax: (212) 505-2375

DESCRIPTION

The Environmental Defense Fund (EDF) is a leading national, nonprofit organization that links science, economics, and law to create solutions to environmental problems.

ACTIVITIES

EDF has testified before Congress and U.S. trade representative (USTR) panels on the potential environmental effects of NAFTA. It has submitted critical evaluations of the draft EPA/SEDUE Integrated Border Environmental Plan for the Mexico-U.S. Border Area, and of the USTR's interagency Review of U.S.-Mexico Environmental Issues. EDF has primarily urged that any economic benefits accruing from NAFTA be partially directed toward increased environmental protection in the border area and beyond. A senior EDF staff member represents the environmental nongovernmental community of the U.S. delegation at the Organization of Economic Cooperation and Development (OECD) meetings. In order to reconcile goals of preserving exhaustible natural resources and pursuing liberalized trade reform, EDF is committed to monitoring GATT's Working Group on Trade and Environment.

RESOURCES

- *The Border Environment and Free Trade*, by Peter M. Emerson and Elizabeth W. Bourbon. 1991. 16 pages. $5.
- *North American Free Trade: A Survey of Environmental Concerns and Solutions*, by Peter M. Emerson (with Raymond F. Mikesell). 1991. 10 pages. $5.
- *Integrating Environmental Protection and North American Free Trade*, by Peter M. Emerson. 1992. 10 pages. $5.

OTHER OFFICES

Environmental Defense Fund-Texas
1800 Guadalupe, Suite A
Austin, TX 78701
Phone: (512) 478-5161
Fax: (512) 478-8140
Contact: Pete Emerson or Jim Marston

Environmental Defense Fund-California
5655 College Ave.
Oakland, CA 94618
Phone: (510) 658-8008
Fax: (510) 658-0630

Environmental Defense Fund-DC
1875 Connecticut, NW #1016
Washington, DC 20009
Phone: (202) 387-3500
Contact: Jake Coldwell

Environmental Health Coalition*

1717 Kettner Blvd. Ste #100
San Diego, CA 92101
Phone: (619) 235-0281
Fax: (619) 232-3670
Contact: Diane Takvorian/José Bravo

DESCRIPTION

This community-based education and policy-advocacy organization is dedicated to preventing illness resulting from exposure to toxic chemicals in the community, the workplace, or the home. It collaborates with groups in Tijuana on issues related to *maquiladoras*.

RESOURCES

- *ToxInformer*. Bimonthly newsletter.

Environmental Safety Committee

Institute for Manufacturing and Materials Management
901 Education Bldg.
500 W. University Ave.
University of Texas at El Paso
El Paso, TX 79968
Phone: (915) 747-5299
Fax: (915) 747-5437

DESCRIPTION

This committee grew out of an assessment of the environmental safety of the greater El Paso border area by a binational cross-section of environmental and hazardous materials professionals.

RESOURCES

- *Southwest Border Infrastructure Initiative*. Report of the Environmental Safety Committee. September 1991.

Environment and Democracy Campaign (EDC)*

224 E. 7th St. #11
New York, NY 10009
Phone: (212) 353-0262
Fax: (212) 995-0653
Contact: Dave Henson

DESCRIPTION

The Environment and Democracy Campaign was founded in 1991 as an outgrowth of the former Environmental Project on Central America (EPOCA). EDC is a collaborative project and serves as international program coordinator for both the National Toxics Campaign Fund in Boston and the Highlander Research and Education Center in New Market, Tennessee. EDC was created to combat the new threats posed to labor and community health by the growing international mobility of toxin-producing industries.

ACTIVITIES

EDC's programs consist of: U.S., third world, and Eastern European exchanges and delegations of grassroots activists; documentation and distribution of popular education materials in the United States; and coordination of domestic and international dialogue in order to build strategies for local activists to respond to the global dimensions of the toxics crisis.

Friends of the Earth (FOE)*

Northwest Office
4512 University Way NE
Seattle, WA 98105
Phone: (206) 633-1661
Fax: (206) 633-1935
Email: foewase
Contact: Andrea Durbin

DESCRIPTION

Friends of the Earth is an international, environmental organization founded in 1969. In 1989 it merged with the Oceanic Society and the Environmental Policy Institute. Friends of the Earth has affiliated organizations in 43 countries and works on a wide range of national and international environmental issues.

ACTIVITIES

Friends of the Earth's International Trade Project pressures U.S. agencies that regulate trade, to consider the social and environmental effects of trade.

LINKS

FOE cooperates with environmental groups in Canada regarding the free trade debate.

RESOURCES

- *A Comprehensive North American Trade Agreement*. Statement of David E. Ortman on behalf of Friends of the Earth, National Wildlife Federation, and the Texas Center for Policy Studies. February 1991.
- *Environmental Concerns Related to the U.S.-Mexico-Canada Free Trade Agreement*. February 1991. List endorsed by Arizona Toxics Information, Community Nutrition Institute, Fair Trade Campaign, Friends of the Earth-U.S., Institute for Agriculture and Trade Policy, National Family Farm Coalition, National Toxics Campaign, National Wildlife Federation, Natural Resources Defense Council, Pollution Probe-Canada, and the Texas Center for Policy Studies.

OTHER OFFICES

Friends of the Earth
218 D St. SE, 2nd Floor
Washington, DC 20003
Phone: (202) 544-2600
Fax: (202) 543-4710
Email: (EcoNet) foedc
Contact: Alejax Hittle

Greenpeace

1436 U St. NW
Washington, DC 20009
Phone: (202) 319-2458
Fax: (202) 462-4507
Contact: Cam Duncan

DESCRIPTION

This international environmental organization, with offices in the United States, Mexico, and Canada, focuses on global environmental issues such as transborder dumping of hazardous wastes. It is one of the most radical environmental groups, with a pronounced internationalist and third world perspective. Greenpeace is in the process of establishing a Mexico City office—contact Fernando Bejarano (see p. 74).

ACTIVITIES

Not actively involved in the NAFTA debate, Greenpeace has closely monitored the effects of GATT and multilateral lending on the environment.

RESOURCES

- *Greenpeace Magazine*. Of special interest is "Trading Away the Planet," September/October 1990.
- A study on the environmental implications of free trade with Mexico.

Highlander Research and Education Center*

1959 Highlander Way
New Market, TN 37802
Phone: (615) 933-3443/45
Fax: (615) 933-3424
Email: (Econet) jmcalevey
Contact: Jane McAlevey, Dave Henson, or Florence Gardner

DESCRIPTION

The Highlander Center seeks to create educational experiences that empower people to take democratic leadership toward fundamental change. The center is committed to working with grassroots community groups in Appalachia and the deep South to resolve pressing social problems through collective action. Highlander's programs span the areas of environmental economics, youth, community environmental health (CEHP), culture, and Southern and Appalachia leadership training. Over the past decade, the CEHP has become Highlander's largest program.

ACTIVITIES

Highlander promotes grassroots education about the impact of NAFTA on communities, sponsors exchanges between jobless Americans and those employed by the *maquiladoras*, and motivates Appalachian communities to become involved in improving their respective situations (i.e. unemployment, exploitation). The CEHP organizes "Stop the Polluters, Save the Planet" workshops.

LINKS

Highlander's International Project works closely with the Fair Trade Campaign and the Citizen Trade Watch Campaign as a consumer and environmental lobby against

NAFTA. As part of their International Project, the Highlander Center established, jointly with the National Toxics Campaign Fund, the Environment and Democracy Campaign (EDC).

RESOURCES

- *The Highlander Report*. Quarterly. Available for a small donation.
- *From the Mountain to the Maquiladoras*, by John Gaventa. Study of the causes and impact of worker dislocation with information on the changing regional and Tennessee economy. 1988. $7.50
- *Taking Charge: A Hands-On Guide to Dealing with the Threat of Plant Closings and Supporting Laid-Off Workers*, compiled by Tennessee Industrial Renewal Network. 1991. $20

Mexico-U.S. Committee on Occupational and Environmental Health*

National Safe Workplace Institute
122 S. Michigan Ave. #1450
Chicago, IL 60603
Phone: (312) 939-0690
Fax: (312) 939-8105
Contact: Joseph A. Kinney, Executive Director

DESCRIPTION

This organization is composed of physicians, epidemiologists, and job-health professionals from both Mexico and the United States. They review data and explore ways to improve Mexico's responsiveness to problems of occupational and environmental health, attempting to create and sustain a dialogue between health professionals in both nations.

ACTIVITIES

In 1991, the National Safe Workplace Institute testified before Congress on several occasions.

RESOURCES

- *Crisis At Our Doorstep: Occupational and Environmental Health Implications for Mexico-U.S.-Canada Trade Negotiations*. $23, includes shipping.

National Toxics Campaign Fund (NTCF)*

1168 Commonwealth Ave.
Boston, MA 02134
Phone: (617) 232-0327
Fax: (617) 232-3945
Contact: Public Relations Director

DESCRIPTION

This environmental research, education, and organizing group boasts a network of more than 1,500 community, state, and regional groups, and more than 75,000 individual members. Fueled by the commitment of citizens poisoned by toxic chemicals, NTCF educates and urges the general public to support groundbreaking pollution-prevention measures.

ACTIVITIES

In 1990, NTCF and its affiliate, the Citizens' Environmental Laboratory, visited several cities along the northern Mexico border to test industrial discharges and receiving waters, and to research water quality and public policies regarding four border waterways: the Río Grande, the Nogales Wash, the New River, and the Tijuana River.

LINKS

It co-sponsors the Environment and Democracy Campaign with the Highlander Research and Education Center.

RESOURCES

- An EPA-certified Citizens' Environmental Lab capable of testing for thousands of soil, air, and water pollutants. This service is available to individuals and groups for a modest fee.
- *Border Trouble: Rivers in Peril*, by Sanford J. Lewis, Marco Kaltofen, and Gregory Ormsby. A 57-page report on water pollution due to industrial development in northern Mexico. May 1991, $15.
- *The Good Neighbor Strategy in the 1990's*, by Sanford J. Lewis. Booklet. $3.
- *Toxics Times*. Quarterly Magazine. $15/yr.
- *Communities in Resistance*. Bimonthly. $15/yr.

National Wildlife Federation*

1400 16th St. NW
Washington, DC 20036-2266
Phone: (202) 797-6602/6800
Fax: (202) 797-6646
Contact: Lynn Greenwalt or Stewart Hudson, International Programs Division.

ACTIVITIES

The National Wildlife Federation, through its Trade and Environment Program, was one of the first conservation organizations to draw attention to the environmental consequences of NAFTA. The federation has researched how environmental concerns can best be integrated into NAFTA, and this material has been used in national lobbying. The federation's Trade and Environment Program contends that sustainable development through trade can only occur if environmental issues are directly integrated into existing and future trade agreements and accords

LINKS

In response to development by multilateral banks, and building on contacts with groups in Mexico and Canada, the federation outlined what has become the basic environmental agenda for NAFTA talks.

RESOURCES

- *Trade and the Environment: Information Packet*. Includes: *Environmental Concerns Related to a United States-Mexico-Canada Free Trade Agreement* (November 1990);

Trade, Environment, and the Pursuit of Sustainable Development (November 1991), and *Environmental Principles related to Trade Agreements*. National Wildlife Federation. 1992.

- *Remarks by Stewart Hudson, Legislative Representative, International Program, at a Congressional Staff Briefing on the U.S.-Mexico Free Trade Agreement*. January 1991. 20 pages. $3.

Natural Resources Defense Council (NRDC)*

1350 New York Ave. NW #300
Washington, DC 20005
Phone: (202) 783-7800
Fax: (202) 783-5917
Contact: Glenn T. Prickett, International Program Associate, or Justin Ward, Senior Resource Specialist

DESCRIPTION

The NRDC is a national, nonprofit, public-interest organization dedicated to preserving the earth's natural resources and improving the quality of the human environment. With offices in New York City, Washington (DC), San Francisco, Los Angeles, and Hawaii, the NRDC combines legal action, scientific research, and citizen education in its environmental protection program. The NRDC has more than 170,000 members and donors in the United States and abroad. Its work includes: air and water quality, energy policy, public-lands and coastal-zone management, sustainable forestry and agriculture, toxics and pesticides, the urban environment, global warming, ozone depletion, trade and the environment, and international environmental issues.

RESOURCES

- *Environmental Review of NAFTA*. Comments to Charles Ries, Deputy Assistant U.S. Trade Representative for North American Affairs on the proposed approach to the Administration's plans for an environmental review of NAFTA, by Glenn T. Prickett and Justin Ward on behalf of Community Nutrition Institute, Environmental Defense Fund, Public Citizen, Sierra Club, and the Texas Center for Policy Studies. July 1991. For publications contact New York office at (212) 727-2700.

Pesticide Action Network (PAN)*

North America Regional Center (PAN-NARC)
965 Mission St. # 514
San Francisco, CA 94103
Phone: (415) 541-9140
Fax: (415) 541-9253
Email: (EcoNet) panna
Contact: Monica Moore

DESCRIPTION

This international coalition of citizen's groups and individuals opposes the misuse and unnecessary use of pesticides. PAN provides coordination, resources, and networking support to people working for safe pest control internationally. Established in 1982, PAN networks over 300 organizations in some 50 countries, coordinated by seven regional centers.

ACTIVITIES

PAN-NARC sponsors a pesticide-reduction project jointly with its office in Mexico (RAPAM) to connect Mexican strawberry growers (in Zamora, Michoacán) with U.S. organic-strawberry growers for training in organic techniques.

RESOURCES

- *Global Pesticide Campaigner*. Quarterly thematic journal featuring news and analysis of international pesticide problems and alternatives, with a focus on citizen action. $25/yr. for individuals and organizations; $15 for low-income individuals; $50 for government agencies and libraries; $100 for corporations.
- *Action Alerts*. As needed. $2 each, free to affiliates and donors.
- *The Pesticide Code Monitor*, by Gretta Goldenman and Sarojini Rengam. 1989. A training manual for activists with practical tips for investigating pesticide use and problems at the local level. 156 pages. $15.
- *Monitoring the International Code of Conduct on the Distribution and Use of Pesticides in North America*, by Marion Moses, M.D., prepared by the Pesticide Education and Action Project. 1988. A field survey of pesticide-related working conditions in the United States and Canada. 25 pages. $5.
- *The Death of Ramón González*, by Angus Wright, PAN-NARC Board Member. A moving study of the human and ecological cost of international agribusiness and agricultural development schemes in Mexico.
- PAN-NARC's Pesticide Information Clearinghouse. 8,000 monographs, articles, slides, and videos, supplemented by a referral network.

Sierra Club*

408 C St. NE
Washington, DC 20002
Phone: (202) 675-6276
Contact: John Audley

DESCRIPTION

This national conservation organization has local chapters throughout the United States and an autonomous branch in Canada. Although not opposing the free trade concept, it has been critical of NAFTA negotiations because of their closed-door character and their lack of attention to environmental concerns.

ACTIVITIES

The Sierra Club has decided that involvement in trade issues is vital to environmental conservation and has established a special office on trade, as well as organizing several forums on U.S.-Mexico environmental issues with Mexican counterparts. The Sierra Club offers comments to the EPA's Trade and Environment Committee concerning NAFTA as well as other international agreements, including the ongoing GATT negotiations. The Sierra Club Office in San Francisco sponsors wilderness expeditions and trail clean-ups in Mexico.

LINKS

It participates in broad trade-related citizen coalitions such as MODTLE, and is beginning through its international office to establish working relationships with Mexican and Canadian environmental groups.

RESOURCES

- *Review of EPA/SEDUE Integrated Border Environmental Plan.* Free.
- *Trade and Environment: A Critique of the U.S.T.R.'s "Review of U.S./Mexico Environmental Issues,"* by Raymond Mikesell and Michael McCloskey. December 1991.
- *A Critique of the GATT Secretariat Report on Trade and Environment*, by John Audley. April 1992. Free.
- *A Critique of the February 21, 1992 draft of the "North American Free Trade Agreement,"* by John Audley. April 1992.

Texas Center for Policy Studies (TCPS)*

PO Box 2618
Austin, TX 78701
Phone: (512) 474-0811
Fax: (512) 478-8140
Contact: Mary Kelly, Executive Director

DESCRIPTION

The Texas Center for Policy Studies (TCPS) is a nonprofit organization offering research, organizing, technical assistance, and policy development on a variety of state, national, and regional environmental issues. Its principle is that the adoption or alteration of economic development and financial policies must take into account environmental and public-health consequences.

ACTIVITIES

Ensuring that the environmental implications of greater integration are addressed within any trade agreement is one objective of TCPS's Free Trade Watch (FTW) project. Initiated in early 1991, as leaders in Mexico and the United States quickly sought to forge a trade pact, the FTW project includes efforts to document the potential environmental impacts of a free trade agreement, and to exchange the information with environmental and community groups involved in the economic-integration debate on both sides of the border. Work focuses on problems of water scarcity and contamination in the border area, as well as options for protecting smaller-scale agricultural producers in both Texas and northern Mexico.

Through its Binational Project, the TCPS and Bioconservación—a Mexican environmental organization based in Monterrey—have developed a network of environmental and community organizations in Texas and the four bordering states of Mexico to address environmental and development issues common to both sides of the border. The project has established two task forces to address issues of water supply, water quality, forestry development, and habitat destruction. The network structure allows groups in both countries to draw on the expertise of their counterparts in addressing problems such as over-allocation of water supplies, the increased use and transport of toxic chemicals, improper waste-disposal practices, and the lack of a sound water and wastewater infrastructure for many communities on both sides of the border.

RESOURCES

- *A Response to the Bush Administration's Environmental Action Plan for Free Trade Negotiations with Mexico.* May 1991. Free.
- *Discussion Paper: Mexico-U.S. Free Trade Negotiations and the Environment: Exploring the Issues*, by the TCPS and the Border Ecology Project. January 1991. $10.

- *Evaluation of the Forestry Development Project of the World Bank in the Sierra Madre Occidental in Chihuahua and Durango, Mexico*, by Richard Lowerre. November 1990. $5.
- *Overview of Environmental Issues Associated with Maquiladora Development along the Texas-Mexico Border*. October 1990. $5.
- *The Maquiladora Boom on the Texas-Mexico Border: Environmental and Public Health Implications and Potential Legal Remedies*, by Mary E. Kelly and Richard Lowerre. June 1990. Out of print.
- *Mexico-United States-Canada Free Trade Negotiations and the Environment*. February 1991. Remarks of Mary E. Kelly before the Senate Finance Committee on behalf of the National Wildlife Federation, the National Toxics Campaign, Friends of the Earth, the Border Ecology Project, and Arizona Toxics Information.

World Environment Center*

419 Park Ave. S. #1800
New York, NY 10016
Phone: (212) 683-4700
Contact: Tony Marcil, President

DESCRIPTION

The group has been working with the Mexican government and private industry to design and fund three wastewater-treatment facilities for Ciudad Juárez. Construction is expected to begin in summer 1992.

RESOURCES

- *Environmental, Health, and Housing Needs and Nonprofit Groups in the U.S.-Mexico Border Area*, by Gail Sevrens. A directory prepared for the Environmental Protection Agency under a cooperative agreement with the World Environment Center. June 1992.

World Wildlife Fund (WWF)/The Conservation Foundation

1250 24th St. NW
Washington, DC 20037
Phone: (202) 293-4800
Contact: William K. Reilly, President, or Lydia Anderson, Manager of Public Information.

DESCRIPTION

World Wildlife Fund is a leading private U.S. organization working worldwide to protect endangered wildlife and wildlands. Its top priority is conservation of the tropical forests of Latin America, Asia, and Africa.

ACTIVITIES

WWF is action-oriented, supporting individuals and institutions that conduct practical, hands-on conservation projects. It has taken the lead in a nongovernmental task force to help the U.S. government prepare a Biological Diversity Strategy for developing countries. Through its Training and Management for Sustainable Development Project, WWF has worked in four countries—Costa Rica, Brazil, Mexico, and Chile—to strengthen the capacity of local institutions to analyze and manage critical issues of environment and development. Other specific projects in Mexico include: 1) Monarch Butterfly Overwintering Habitat Conservation; 2) Conservation and Development Efforts, Tuxtla Mountains, southern Veracruz; 3) Tropical Rain Forest Conservation, Chiapas (with the Instituto de Historia Natural); 4) Forage Production Project, Quintana Roo, Mexico; 5) Institutional Support for Monarca; and 6) Sierra Laguna Biosphere Reserve Management, Baja California Sur.

LINKS

World Wildlife Fund is formally affiliated with The Conservation Foundation (identical president and boards), a nonprofit environmental-research organization that brings to the affiliation expertise in social science and policy analysis. The foundation assists in the development of nongovernmental organizations in Latin America such as Restauración Ambiental, a Mexican counterpart.

RESOURCES

- *Mexico's Living Endowment: An Overview of Biological Diversity/Patrimonio Vivo de México: Un Diagnóstico de la Diversidad Biológica*. Spanish/English. Published by Conservation International in collaboration with the Instituto Nacional de Investigación sobre Recursos Bióticos, INIREB (Mexico). 1989.

PART IV

Advocacy Organizations

INTRODUCTION

Nonprofit organizations that promote human rights and advocate social justice for native people, women, and immigrants are important participants in the cross-border networks developing in North America. Most of these advocacy organizations existed long before the NAFTA negotiations. Typically, however, they focused on their own issue areas, often confining their concerns to just one country. Their recent involvement in bi- and trinational relations stems from the convergence of their usual interests with issues arising from the trinational trade negotiations.

There are a number of ways in which these advocacy organizations contribute to the debate over NAFTA and promote the interests of their constituencies. Many of them conduct research and publicize information useful to activists and policymakers. The effects of NAFTA on economic and trade policy, development, immigrant and human rights laws, and cultural and indigenous identity have been among the topics addressed by these groups. Other organizations are committed to direct political action, sponsoring conferences and forums intended to mobilize activists. Still others function as think tanks for the popular sector, devising alternatives to NAFTA.

The linking of research with advocacy has made these organizations influential in the nongovernmental and grassroots sectors. This growing social impact explains why government agencies and academic institutions increasingly consult the reports and other resources of the advocacy organizations.

1. CANADA

Canadian Council for International Co-operation (CCIC)*

1 Nicholas St. #300
Ottawa, ON K1N 7B7
Phone: (613) 236-4547
Fax: (613) 236-2188
Email: (PeaceNet) ccic.ott (WEB/GeoNet/AlterNet) ccic
Contact: Randy Keats

DESCRIPTION

This umbrella coalition of 130 Canadian voluntary organizations is committed to achieving global development in a peaceful and healthy environment, with social justice, human dignity, and participation for all. Membership includes both secular and religious-based development organizations drawn from cooperatives, unions, professional associations, and educational organizations. CCIC receives matching funds from the Canadian International Development Agency.

ACTIVITIES

CCIC engages in networking, leadership, information dissemination, training, and coordination. It also acts as an advocate for its members before government, the media, and the public. The council supports development programs in Africa, Asia, and Latin America, and produces public-education programs for Canadians about development and the third world.

LINKS

CCIC works in close consultation with regional and provincial that which include: the Atlantic Regional Committee, Association québécoise des organismes de co-opération internationale (AQOCI), the Development Education Coordinating Council of Alberta; and Councils for International Cooperation in British Columbia, Saskatchewan, Manitoba, and Ontario.

RESOURCES

- *The I.D. Profile: A Who's Who and What's What of International Development.* A guide to Canadian nongovernmental organizations involved in third world development. CCIC, 1989. $51 for members, $59 for nonmembers.
- *Au Courant.* Monthly newsletter. Reports on CCIC's activities and current affairs related to international development. Free to member organizations, $25/yr. for nonmembers.
- *GATT and Food Security: A Canadian Perspective.* A commissioned report by David Gilles. Free.

Citizens Concerned About Free Trade (CCAFT)

PO Box 8052
Saskatoon, SK S7K 4R7
Phone: (306) 244-5757
Fax: (306) 244-3790
Contact: David Orchard, National Chairperson, or Marjaleena Repol, National Organizer

DESCRIPTION

The CCAFT is a national, nonpartisan, citizens organization opposed to the U.S.-Canada Free Trade Agreement and to foreign control in Canada. Its aim is the repeal of the agreement and the building of an independent Canada.

ACTIVITIES

The group conducts public information meetings and debates across the nation on the free trade agreement and its effect on Canadian sovereignty, the economy, and national well-being.

RESOURCES

- *True North*. Bimonthly newspaper
- *Manifest Destiny and the Free Trade Agreement*, by David Orchard. Fall 1992.

Council of Canadians (COC)*

251 Laurier Ave. W. #1006
Ottawa, ON K1P 5J6
Phone: (613) 233-2773
Fax: (613) 233-6776
Contact: Catherine Morrison, Executive Director

DESCRIPTION

This national, nonpartisan, public-interest organization devoted to the enhancement and preservation of Canadian sovereignty and political independence has 20,000 members. The COC monitors Canadian domestic and foreign policies, lobbies decision-makers to protect Canadian interests, and promotes alternatives for an independent Canada in a world community of nations.

LINKS

The Council of Canadians is a member of Action Canada Network.

RESOURCES

- *Parcel of Rogues: How Free Trade is Failing Canada*, by Maude Barlow. 1990. 250 pages.
- *Canadian Perspectives*. Three issues/yr. free with membership. $100/yr. for non-members.
- *Take Back the Nation*, by Maude Barlow and Bruce Campbell. Key Porter Books, 1991.

Ecumenical Coalition for Economic Justice*

11 Madison Ave.
Toronto, ON M5R 2S2
Phone: (416) 921-4615
Fax: (416) 924-5356
Contact: Dennis Howlett

DESCRIPTION

The coalition engages in research, education, and political action on global issues of economic justice. Current priorities include NAFTA negotiations, the global debt crisis, the future of women's work, and social-movement coalitions.

ACTIVITIES

The Coalition Exchange Project facilitates interaction among social-movement coalitions in Canada, South Africa, the Philippines, and Mexico through a series of seminars and the publication of a book.

LINKS

The Ecumenical Coalition is active in Common Frontiers, Action Canada Network, and the Canadian Council of Churches.

RESOURCES

- *Economic Justice Report*. Quarterly. $20 for individuals, $35 for organizations.

Jesuit Centre for Social Faith and Justice (Central America Team)*

947 Queen St. E.
Toronto, ON M4M 2H3
Phone: (416) 469-1123
Fax: (416) 469-3579
Contact: Joe Gunn, Coordinator

DESCRIPTION

The centre is involved in research, advocacy, and public education on Canadian foreign policy in Central America. It also provides minor funding of projects in Mexico and Central America.

ACTIVITIES

The centre organizes forums with invited guests from Mexico, Central America, and the Caribbean.

LINKS

Funder and member of the board of Common Frontiers, the centre also works closely with CAPA (Canada-Caribbean-Central America Policy Alternatives), a group dedicated to research on and for Central America and the Caribbean, and to the development of viable policy initiatives for Canada. Among the research interests of CAPA are Canadian investment and trade, the role of banks in the region, and Canada-U.S. relations, especially as they affect policy toward the Central America/Caribbean region.

RESOURCES

- *Central America Update*. Bimonthly newsletter co-published with the Latin American Working Group (see LAWG for rates, below).
- *As the Empire Grows: Canada-U.S.-Mexico Free Trade*. Co-produced with Common Frontiers and the Metro Labour Education Centre. $3 for individuals, $4.50 for institutions. *As the Empire Grows* was a special issue of *The Moment* (Vol. 5, No. 1, Fall 1991). Quarterly newsletter. $9/yr. for individuals, $13/yr. for institutions.
- *Free Trade in Central America*. Fall 1992 issue of the *CAPA Occasional Papers*. $20.

Latin American Working Group (LAWG)

PO Box 2207, Station P
Toronto, ON M5S 2T2
Phone: (416) 533-4221
Fax: (416) 924-5356
Contact: Fern Valin

DESCRIPTION

This nonprofit organization conducts research and educational programs designed to strengthen ties between Canadian and Latin American peoples.

ACTIVITIES

In addition to facilitating research at its library, LAWG organizes conferences, acts as a liaison between Canadian and Mexican organizations, and engages in political-solidarity networking.

LINKS

Member of Action Canada Network.

RESOURCES

- *Latin American Working Group Letter*. Of special interest is *Open for Business: Canada-Mexico-U.S. Free Trade*, LAWG Letter #45.
- *Central America Update*. Bimonthly newsletter co-published with the Jesuit Centre for Social Faith and Justice. $25/yr. for individuals, $30/yr. for institutions, $15/yr. for students and unemployed.

Mujer a Mujer — Toronto*

606 Shaw St.
Toronto, ON M6G 3L6
Phone: (416) 532-8584
Email: (WEB) perg
U.S. mailing address: PO Box 12322, San Antonio, TX 78212
Contact: Lynda Yanz

DESCRIPTION

This collective of Mexican, U.S., Canadian, and Caribbean women promotes communication, exchange, and strategic networking among activist women throughout the region. They engage in analysis, education, and action related to the impact of structural adjustment, continental restructuring, and free trade on women's lives and struggles.

ACTIVITIES

In Mexico during February 1992, Mujer a Mujer collaborated with the Mexican group MAS (Mujeres en Acción Sindical—Women in Union Action) to organize the first trinational working-women's conference on free trade and continental integration. Over 110 women from the United States, Canada, and Mexico attended, representing unions, women's and community groups, church and justice organizations, research and policy institutes as well as national coalitions and networks.

LINKS

Linda Yanz also chairs the Global Strategies Committee, a project of the National Action Committee on the Status of Women (see below).

RESOURCES

- *Correspondencia*. Trinational Spanish/English bulletin. Three times per year. $10/yr., $6/yr. low income.

National Action Committee on the Status of Women (NAC)

344 Bloor St. W. #505
Toronto, ON M5S 3A7
Phone: (416) 759-5252
Fax: (416) 759-5370
Contact: Judy Rebick, President

DESCRIPTION

This umbrella group of some 500 women's organizations includes: women's committees from union locals, as well as national and provincial levels; women's shelters and centers; legal organizations; antipoverty groups; organizations of women of color; immigrant women's projects; lesbian organizations; and professional women's associations. NAC is officially nonaligned to any political party but the resolutions adopted at its national conventions place it in strong opposition to the conservative federal government. It has worked on issues of violence against women, reproductive rights, poverty, and working women.

ACTIVITIES

NAC's Women and Work Committee deals with issues of continental integration, pay equity, and training. The Global Strategies Committee monitors the impact of free trade and continental restructuring on women, and develops solidarity with women's groups in the United States and Latin America.

LINKS

Member of Action Canada Network.

National Farmers Union

250-C 2nd Ave. S.
Saskatoon, SK S7K 2M1
Phone: (306) 652-9465
Fax: (306) 664-6226
Contact: Wayne Easter or Terry Pugh

ACTIVITIES

It has active connections with Mexican (Frente Democrático Campesino de Chihuahua) and U.S. farmers.

LINKS

Member of Action Canada Network.

OXFAM Canada

251 Laurier Ave. W. #301
Ottawa, ON K1P 5J6
Phone: (613) 237-5236
Fax: (613) 237-0524
Contact: John Foster

DESCRIPTION

This international development agency has projects and offices in Canada, the United States, and Mexico.

ACTIVITIES

It engages in development work and does some lobbying and networking.

LINKS

Affiliated with Action Canada Network.

World Council of Indigenous Peoples (WCIP)*

100 Argyle St. #2
Ottawa, ON K2P 1B6
Phone: (613) 230-9030
Fax: (613) 230-9340
Contact: Rodrigo Contreras

DESCRIPTION

The objectives of the World Council of Indigenous Peoples are: to promote the unity of and exchange of information among indigenous peoples of the world to combat ethnocide directed against them; and to ensure amicable relations between these native peoples and their geographic neighbors. The WCIP has consultative status with the Economic and Social Council, the International Labour Organization (ILO), and UNESCO of the United Nations.

ACTIVITIES

Its projects center on economic and social development, inter-institutional policymaking forums, information dissemination, and quincentennial analysis.

2. MEXICO

Academia Mexicana de Derechos Humanos (AMDH)*

Filosofía y Letras 88
Col. Copilco Universidad
México, D.F. 04360
Phone: (5) 6-58-72-79
Fax: (5) 6-58-58-53
Contact: Sergio Aguayo Quezada, President

DESCRIPTION

The Mexican Academy for Human Rights (AMDH) champions the human rights of Latin American immigrants in North America through its Immigrant Studies Program. The AMDH gathers information, organizes academic conferences, seminars and workshops, and formulates proposals for the defense of human rights.

LINKS

The AMDH is part of the Convergence of Civil Organizations for Democracy.

RESOURCES

- *Derechos Humanos*. Bimonthly bulletin.
- *Manual de Derechos Humanos de los Indígenas*.
- *Manual de Observación de las Elecciones*. Cost varies, from $5,000 to $25,000 M.N.

Asamblea de Barrios*

Calle I, Edif. 21 #24
Unidad FOVISSSTE Miramontes
México, D.F. 04800
Phone: (5) 6-84-74-04/5-26-60-98
Fax: (5) 6-84-74-04
Contact: *Superbarrio Gómez*, Marco Rascón, or Francisco Saucedo

DESCRIPTION

This grassroots organization, formed by homeless families and neighborhood associations, has struggled for housing and democracy both in Mexico City and in the country as a whole. Asamblea de Barrios (the Assembly of Neighborhoods) is led by a human "*Superbarrio*" (a masked social fighter with a red and yellow wrestler's outfit—a Superman parody), a popular symbol of Mexico City's urban movement battles.

ACTIVITIES

Superbarrio fights for decent housing for the poor by applying direct pressure on Mexico City's political leaders, on government authorities in charge of official housing programs, and on the Asamblea de Representantes (a Mexico City representative body that can post notices and suggest regulations but not pass laws). In addition, Asamblea de Barrios organizes wrestling matches wherein *Superbarrio* symbolically confronts "evil landlords"—the archenemies of all renters. As part of his international activities,

Superbarrio has traveled to the United States, sponsored by Mexico-U.S. Dialogos, where he has met with undocumented workers, Chicano organizations, agricultural day laborers, congressional representatives, and city councilpersons. He has also participated in meetings of The Other Economic Summit.

LINKS

The Assembly of Neighborhoods is linked with Cuauhtémoc Cárdenas and the Party of the Democratic Revolution (PRD).

Centro Binacional de Derechos Humanos*

Joaquín Clausel #4-4
Desarrollo Urbano
Río Tijuana A.P. 848
Tijuana, B.C. 22000
Phone: (66) 34-33-22
U.S. mailing address: PO Box 3395, San Diego, CA 92163
U.S. phone/fax: (619) 295-2830
Contact: Víctor Clark-Alfaro

DESCRIPTION

Centro Binacional de Derechos Humanos (the Binational Center for Human Rights) is a nongovernmental, social service organization dedicated to the investigation, documentation, and denunciation of human rights violations committed against indigenous, peasant, child, and Central American immigrants. It specializes in cases of torture.

ACTIVITIES

The center organizes conferences and classes to sensitize people about human rights, exchanges information trinationally about immigrants and human rights, and offers free medical and legal services.

LINKS

The group is part of the Permanent Seminar for Chicano and Border Studies, and has links to the Sanctuary Movement and the National Network for Immigrant and Refugee Rights.

RESOURCES

- *Informe Anual de Derechos Humanos*. U.S. $4.50.

Centro de Estudios Fronterizos y de Promoción de los Derechos Humanos (CEFPRODHAC)*

Zaragoza 650 #4
Col. Centro
Ciudad Reynosa, Tamps.
Phone: (892) 2-24-41
Fax: (892) 2-24-41
U.S. mailing address: 21 E. Coma #178, Hidalgo, TX 78557
Contact: Arturo Solís, President

DESCRIPTION

Centro de Estudios Fronterizos y de Promoción de los Derechos Humanos (the Center for Border Studies and Human Rights) works in the defense, counsel and promotion of human rights of Mexican and Central American immigrants, particularly along the Tamaulipas border with the United States.

ACTIVITIES

The center investigates and gathers information about diverse aspects of the border: religious sects, *maquiladoras*, the free trade agreement, children's rights, narcotraffic, unreported crimes, and human rights issues.

LINKS

The center belongs to the National Coordinator of NGOs in Support of Central American Refugees, the Maquiladoras Network, the National Network on Free Trade, and the Human Rights Network.

RESOURCES

- *Boletín Informativo*. Monthly.

Comisión Mexicana de Defensa y Promoción de los Derechos Humanos*

Tabasco 262 #201
Col. Roma
México, D.F. 06700
Phone: (5) 5-25-25-45
Fax: (5) 2-08-30-44
Contact: Mariclaire Acosta, President

DESCRIPTION

Comisión Mexicana de Defensa y Promoción de los Derechos Humanos (the Mexican Commission for the Defense and Promotion of Human Rights) investigates human rights violations in Mexico, whether committed by the state or by any of its judicial organisms.

LINKS

The group's president, Mariclaire Acosta, is also executive director of The Other Economic Summit (TOES). The Commission belongs to the Network of Civil Organizations for Human Rights "All the Rights to All," the National Network of NGO's for Human Rights, the Convergence of Civil Organizations for Democracy, and the Information Network on Latin American Human Rights.

Coordinadora Nacional de Organizaciones Cafetaleras (CNOC)

Tabasco 262 #301
Col. Roma
México, D.F. 06700
Phone: (5) 5-14-02-05
Fax: (5) 2-07-05-08
Contact: Luis Hernández

DESCRIPTION

CNOC is a national network of 70 *campesino* organizations totaling over 50,000 small coffee producers. Several regional coffee-growing organizations formed CNOC in 1988, largely in response to declining government support for small growers. The group conducts market and technical research, develops alternative forms of financing, and trains growers in all steps of the production and processing of coffee.

ACTIVITIES

In addition to its efforts to find international markets for member growers, CNOC seeks international partners in setting a broader agenda. This agenda includes attaining government policies and international agreements that protect small farmers, encourage sustainable agriculture, and provide stable markets. In this regard CNOC was a Mexican co-sponsor (with UNORCA) of the "Trinational Exchange on Agriculture, the Environment, and the Free Trade Agreement," held in November 1991 in Mexico City. In addition, CNOC and UNORCA have formed the Centro de Estudios para el Cambio del Campo en México (CECCAM), a think tank working on alternative policies and leadership training. (CECCAM address: Tabasco 262 #602.)

Despacho de Orientación y Asesoría Legal (DOAL)

Doctor Carmona y Valle 32 bis
Col. Doctores
México, D.F.
Phone: (5) 5-88-31-80
Contact: Efrén Rodríguez

DESCRIPTION

DOAL is a group of six lawyers who defend workers and low-income groups in the areas of civil law. It works with 30 popular organizations in Mexico City and several other states.

ACTIVITIES

DOAL trains members of urban movements. It has also recently done research on the implications of the changes in the Mexican Constitution effected in order to pave the way for NAFTA.

LINKS

The group belongs to the Convergence of Civil Organizations for Democracy, and the National Association of Democratic Lawyers. DOAL has links with the Legal Defense Fund, the National Association for the Advancement of Colored People (NAACP), the Internship on Human Rights of the Columbia University's Faculty of Law, the National Lawyers Guild, and the Bogotá-based Interamerican Legal Services Association (ILSA). DOAL also has links with Développement et paix.

RESOURCES

- It has published 14 handbooks on legal training for popular organizations.

Equipo Pueblo*

Francisco Field Jurado 51
Col. Independencia
México, D.F. 03630
Phone: (5) 5-39-00-15/55
Fax: (5) 6-72-74-53
Email: (PeaceNet) igc:pueblo
Mailing Address: A.P. 27-467, México, D.F. 06760
Contact: Carlos Heredia or Elio Villaseñor

DESCRIPTION

Equipo Pueblo (the People's Team) is a nongovernmental development organization dedicated to democratic change in Mexico. It provides a wide array of support services to grassroots organizations including: project formulation and funding-proposal guidance, advice to cooperatives on the commercialization of their ventures, popular-education programs and forums for the discussion of current political affairs, coalition building across diverse sectors of popular organizations, and international network promotion between Mexican social organizations and their foreign counterparts.

ACTIVITIES

Specific bi/trinational activities include: 1) *Cross-Border Links*, a trinational project between the People's Team, the Inter-Hemispheric Education Resource Center, and Action Canada Network comprising an annotated, trinational directory of groups interested in cross-border relations as well as a clearinghouse to facilitate communication and information exchange; 2) cooperative work with the Development Group for Alternative Policies to promote Mexican and U.S. alternatives to NAFTA; 3) participation in the NGO's Working Group on the World Bank to expose the environmental and social impact of structural adjustment policies in the third world; 4) collaboration with Mexico-U.S. Dialogos in developing investigative projects, dealing with topics such as the role of NGOs and grassroots movements in U.S.-Mexico relations.

LINKS

Equipo Pueblo works closely with: Red Fondad sobre la Deuda Externa, Fundación El Taller, and Grandes Ciudades de América Latina. It also collaborates with the alternative policies of the Mexican branch of Council 500 Years of Indigenous and Popular Resistance, and the Mexican Action Network on Free Trade (RMALC). The People's Team is part of the Citizen Movement for Democracy (MCD), the National Accord for Democracy (ACUDE), and the Convergence of Civil Organizations for Democracy. In addition, the People's Team participates in the educational campaigns of Développement et paix of Canada.

RESOURCES

- *La Otra Cara de México/The Other Side of Mexico*. Bimonthly bulletin, published in Spanish and English. In Latin America U.S. $10/yr. for individuals, U.S. $18/yr. for institutions. In North America and Europe U.S. $15/yr. for individuals, U.S. $20 for institutions.
- *Revista Pueblo*. Bimonthly. Promotes social and political democracy in Mexico.

- *Cross-Border Links*. Directory of organizations in Mexico, the United States, and Canada with projects related to bi/trinational relationships. Co-produced by the Inter-Hemispheric Education Resource Center, the People's Team, and Action Canada Network. August 1992. U.S. $11.95.

Frente Democrático Campesino de Chihuahua*

Aldama 307 #5
Col. Centro
Chihuahua, Chih. 31000
Phone: (14) 10-61-43
Contact: Víctor Quintana

DESCRIPTION

Frente Democrático Campesino de Chihuahua (the Peasants Democratic Front of Chihuahua) is an organization of 6,000 corn farmers, primarily from *ejidos* (common lands) in central and western Chihuahua. It seeks better prices for corn and other local products, and pursues the social and political democratization of the state of Chihuahua.

ACTIVITIES

The front participates in direct action and political events in Chihuahua as well as in national and international forums.

LINKS

It has binational ties on the northern border of Mexico with the Unión de Trabajadores Agrícolas Fronterizos (UTAF). Trinational ties are maintained with the National Farmers Union both in the United States and in Saskatchewan, Canada, as well as with the Union of Agricultural Producers of Québec. Some Democratic Front members also participate in The Other Economic Summit (TOES).

Fronteras Comunes*

Centro Coordinador de Proyectos Ecuménicos (CECOPE)
Río Niágara 40 bis
Col. Cuauhtémoc
México, D.F. 06500
Phone: (5) 5-11-17-81
Fax: (5) 5-11-17-81
Email: (PeaceNet) cecope
Contact: Víctor Osorio

DESCRIPTION

Fronteras Comunes (Common Frontiers) promotes the discussion and development of alternatives to NAFTA in Mexico, the exchange of information among social organizations and specialists, and the promotion of exchanges and other contacts between Mexico, the United States, and Canada.

LINKS

As the counterpart of Common Frontiers in Canada, the group functions as an active part of the Mexican Action Network on Free Trade (RMALC). It is also closely linked to the Center for Information and Immigration Studies (CIEM), of Ciudad Juárez, Tijuana, Zacatecas, and Reynosa.

Fundación Lázaro Cárdenas*

Dr. Gálvez 33 #303
Col. San Angel
México, D.F. 01000
Phone: (5) 5-48-72-53
Fax: (5) 5-48-72-53
Contact: Adolfo Aguilar Zinser, President, or Jorge Martínez y Almaráz, Director

DESCRIPTION

Fundación Lázaro Cárdenas (Lázaro Cárdenas Foundation) is an autonomous center for research, public opinion, and lobbying formed by Mexican leader Cuauhtémoc Cárdenas.

ACTIVITIES

Through prestigious critics of NAFTA like Adolfo Aguilar Zinser and Jorge Castañeda, the foundation rose in stature following its release in Mexico (in conjunction with the Mexican Action Network on Free Trade) of a classified, official draft NAFTA. Both Castañeda and Zinser are active in academic conferences related to NAFTA throughout the United States as well. Zinser is a member of CISEUA and Castañeda writes for *Proceso*, *Newsweek*, *Los Angeles Times*, and *Le Monde*.

LINKS

The Lázaro Cárdenas Foundation, though independent, has links to the PRD.

Instituto de Estudios para el Desarrollo Rural "Maya"*

Altavista 1
Col. San Angel
México, D.F. 01000
Phone: (5) 5-50-42-03
Fax: (5) 5-50-42-03
Contact: Armando Bartra

DESCRIPTION

Instituto de Estudios para el Desarrollo Rural "Maya" (the Institute of Studies for Rural Development "Maya") is a group of academics specializing in rural issues through more than 80 studies regarding agrarian reality in Mexico. The institute encourages the participation of peasants in rural development and in the revitalization, development, and diffusion of community culture.

ACTIVITIES

The institute engages in interdisciplinary research and popular education as well as advising governmental agencies and social groups. It organizes national conventions, M.A. and Ph.D. academic programs, and multinational research projects.

RESOURCES

- Books, movies, videos and audiovisuals.

Mujer a Mujer*

A.P. 24-553
Col. Roma
México, D.F. 06701
Phone: (5) 2-07-08-34
Fax: (5) 5-84-10-68
Email: (PeaceNet) igc:mam
U.S. mailing address: PO Box 12322, San Antonio, TX 78212
Contact: Mercedes López

DESCRIPTION

Mujer a Mujer (Woman to Woman) organizes exchanges, workshops, tours, and activist retreats to promote strategic connections among grassroots and feminist organizations in Mexico, Canada, and the United States. Its areas of focus are labor and community organizing, Mexicana/Chicana/Latina lesbians, popular health, education, and violence against women. The objectives of Mujer a Mujer are: to support women's organizations in their understanding of the economic restructuring occurring in the region and of its connection to issues related to women and their communities; to enhance the sharing of successful strategies appropriate to an era of international integration; to help develop vital, ongoing forms of communication between women's organizations in Mexico, Canada, the United States, and Central America; and to support the participation of women and the presence of a gender perspective within the broad, national coalitions developing to confront the impact of the investment-centered integration of North American economies.

ACTIVITIES

Jointly with Mujeres en Acción Sindical, Mujer a Mujer organized a trinational women's conference in Mexico of women on the topic: Free Trade and Economic Integration. Participants included representatives from labor, teachers, garment, hospital, bank, university, and electrical workers unions; domestic and *maquila* workers' community-labor organizations; free trade action networks; and research and social justice organizations. Mujer a Mujer is also organizing the conference: Neighborhood Organizing in the Maquila Age, as well as a Chicana-Mexicana Cultural Exchange.

LINKS

Mujer a Mujer is a member of the RMALC, the North American Popular Educators, and the Women's Alternative Economics Network.

RESOURCES

- *Correspondencia*. Quarterly. English and Spanish. U.S. $10.

Regional de Mujeres de la CONAMUP

República de Argentina 63
Col. Centro
México, D.F. 06020
Phone: (5) 5-26-76-29
Contact: Clara Brugada or María Elena González

DESCRIPTION

This is a grassroots organization of housewives from the working-class neighborhoods surrounding Mexico City. They struggle for womens' rights and better housing, and against inflation.

ACTIVITIES

Since 1984, Regional de Mujeres (Women's Regional) members have visited women in San Antonio, New Orleans, Atlanta, St. Louis, Chicago, Philadelphia, Washington, Baltimore, New York City, and Montreal, Canada. They also have hosted women's groups from the National Coalition of the Homeless and from feminist organizations in the United States.

LINKS

As part of the National Coordinating Council of the Urban Popular Movement (CONAMUP), they have organized their trips jointly with the trinational group Mujer a Mujer.

Servicio, Desarrollo y Paz (SEDEPAC)*

Huatusco 39
Col. Roma Sur
México, D.F. 06760
Phone: (5) 5-74-08-92/63-97
Fax: (5) 5-84-38-95
Contact: Rafael Reygadas Robles Gil

DESCRIPTION

Servicio, Desarrollo y Paz (Service, Development and Peace) promotes initiatives that originate in the popular sectors of society, and that seek a more humanitarian, fair, and united society.

ACTIVITIES

SEDEPAC operates programs dealing with *maquiladoras*, Central American refugees, and youth training. Through these programs the group seeks to analyze trinational relations from the perspectives of base communities, nongovernmental organizations (NGOs), local churches, and Mexican civil society in general in order to formulate policies, strategies, and coordinated actions.

LINKS

SEDEPAC is a member of the National Coordinator of NGOs in Support of Central American Refugees, the International Council of Voluntary Agencies, the Convergence of Civil Organizations for Democracy, the Mexican Kellogg Network; the Inter-Institutional Network of Centers of Support; and the RMALC.

RESOURCES

- *Carta de Noticias*. Newsletter with general information about SEDEPAC's projects. Monthly and bilingual.
- *Mexico Insight*. A look at Mexico's problems from the perspective of base communities and NGOs.

Servicios Informativos Procesados (SIPRO)*

Alvaro Obregón 213, piso 2
Col. Roma
México, D.F. 06670
Phone: (5) 5-11-21-51
Fax: (5) 5-11-52-41
Email: (PeaceNet) igc:sipro
Contact: Benjamín Matías Heredia

DESCRIPTION

Servicios Informativos Procesados (Processed Information Services) is a nongovernmental organization (NGO) specializing in the systematization and processing of information. Its analysis of the Mexican situation is well-known by international popular groups and NGOs.

ACTIVITIES

SIPRO organizes grassroots education workshops dealing with the political state of affairs in Mexico, as well as workshops analyzing various sectors of Mexican society.

LINKS

SIPRO is an integral supporter of the RMALC, as well as a member of the Convergence of Civil Organizations for Democracy, and the Inter-Institutional Network of Centers of Support.

RESOURCES

- *Workshop on the National Situation*. Proceedings from grassroots education workshops. Quarterly. $5,000 M.N.
- Information service through the electronic network PeaceNet.
- Data Bank about Mexico with periodical clippings since 1983.

Unión Nacional de Organizaciones Regionales Campesinas Autónomas (UNORCA)

José Antonio Torres 618
Col. Vista Alegre
México, D.F. 06860
Phone: (5) 7-40-48-48
Fax: (5) 7-40-73-93

DESCRIPTION

Representing mostly small landholders, UNORCA has gained influence as the government increasingly avoids traditional and communal farmers represented by the National Confederation of Campesinos (CNC). Although supportive of President Salinas's emphasis on productivity and the private sector, UNORCA seeks government support in the areas of price guarantees, subsidies, credit, and market access.

ACTIVITIES

UNORCA was a Mexican co-sponsor (with CNOC) of the "Trinational Exchange on Agriculture, the Environment, and the Free Trade Agreement" held in November 1991 in Mexico City.

3. UNITED STATES

American Friends Service Committee (AFSC)*

1501 Cherry St.
Philadelphia, PA 19102
Phone: (215) 241-7132
Fax: (215) 241-7275
Contact: Primitivo Rodriguez, National Director, U.S.-Mexico Border Program

DESCRIPTION

This globally recognized institution operates programs of service, advocacy, organizing, education, and development in the United States and abroad. AFSC seeks to root out the causes of violence that lie in poverty and imbalance of wealth and to help establish conditions in which all women and men can live in dignity. AFSC has worked along the Mexico-U.S. border for more than 20 years on programs dealing with health, human rights, and economic development.

ACTIVITIES

AFSC's U.S.-Mexico Border Program documents abuse against immigrants, legal residents, and U.S. citizens by U.S. immigration law-enforcement officials; monitors the social and environmental impact of the *maquiladora* industry; and promotes interchange and cooperation between U.S. and Mexican groups affected by or interested in U.S.-Mexico economic integration. The Border Program conducts its work in close cooperation with community organizations along the U.S. southern border as well as with regional and national networks. The program's main goal is to help build working-people's power to impact public policies, practices, and attitudes that affect their standard of living and quality of life.

The Maquiladora Project (Phoebe McKinney, Director. Phone: [215] 241-7129) is one activity of the U.S.-Mexico Border Program. Its concern is to increase public awareness of the negative impact of *maquiladoras* on workers in both Mexico and the United States. It interacts with binational organizations at the border in support of women workers in the *maquiladoras*. On a national level, it shares information about *maquiladora* issues with journalists, public officials, and other organizations and activists.

Other projects of the U.S.-Mexico Border Program include: the Binational Commission on Human Rights, and the Immigration Law Enforcement Monitoring Project (ILEMP). The latter monitors the Immigration Reform and Control Act of 1986 (IRCA), addresses agricultural worker (migrant) issues as they apply to Immigration and Naturalization Service enforcement, and analyzes housing and labor issues.

LINKS

AFSC is among the most respected of all nonprofit organizations and thus has links and/or membership with most organizations working on Mexico-U.S. relations.

RESOURCES

- *Background and Perspectives on the U.S.-Mexico-Canada Free Trade Talks*. April 1991. 15 pages. $2.50
- *The Global Factory: Analysis and Action for a New Economic Era*. By Rachel Kamel. AFSC, 1990. $7.50; 5 or more $5 each.

- *Sealing Our Borders: The Human Toll.* Third Report by ILEMP analyzing border law enforcement in California, Texas, Arizona, and Florida. February 1992. $2.50 each.

OTHER OFFICES

U.S.-Mexico Border Program*
PO Box 126147
San Diego, CA 92112
Phone: (619) 233-4114
Fax: (619) 233-6247
Contact: Roberto Martínez, Director

Immigration Law Enforcement Monitoring Project (ILEMP)
515 Allen Parkway
Houston, TX 77019
Phone: (713) 524-5428
Fax: (713) 524-8183
Contact: Maria Jimenez, Project Director

Americans for Democracy in Mexico*

PO Box 188031
Sacramento, CA 95818
Phone: (916) 446-3021
Fax: (916) 442-7923
Contact: Albert Rojas

DESCRIPTION

This organization provides information to political, labor, and community groups in the United States about the electoral process in Mexico, the state of human rights, and border and environmental issues.

ACTIVITIES

Americans for Democracy in Mexico organizes trips to Mexico for people willing to serve as independent electoral observers.

Americas Watch Committee*

Human Rights Watch
10951 West Pico Blvd. #203
Los Angeles, CA 90064
Phone: (310) 475-3070
Fax: (310) 475-5613
Email: (PeaceNet) hrwatchla
Contact: Ellen L. Lutz

DESCRIPTION

Americas Watch monitors and promotes observance of free expression and other internationally recognized human rights in Central America, South America, and the Caribbean. It is one of the five regional committees of Human Rights Watch.

LINKS

Americas Watch has a working relationship with the Academia Mexicana de Derechos Humanos and the Centro Binacional de Derechos Humanos.

RESOURCES

- *Human Rights in Mexico, A Policy of Impunity*, by Ellen L. Lutz, California Director of Human Rights Watch, and other Los Angeles-based Human Rights Watch staff members. Report, 1990.
- *Prison Conditions in Mexico*, by Nan Aron. Report, March 1991.

Beyond Borders*

4677 30th St. #214
San Diego, CA 92116
Phone: (619) 280-2976
Contact: Marc A. Worthington or Mary Tong

DESCRIPTION

Beyond Borders is a nonprofit group of organizers providing resources for other organizers and friends of labor. Their publication (of the same name) aims to aid organizers, community activists, and others working for economic and social justice to make the cross-border links for international solidarity so essential to the struggle for change and human betterment.

RESOURCES

- *Beyond Borders*. Quarterly magazine. Information, interviews, and analysis of the current situation. $12/yr.

Center for Ethics and Economic Policy*

2512 9th St. #3
Berkeley, CA 94710
Phone: (510) 549-9931
Fax: (510) 549-9995
Contact: Ron Stief, Director

DESCRIPTION

The center offers training sessions on international economics focusing on trade agreements and international investment. It is also involved in direct action regarding economic policy and trade ethics.

LINKS

Member of the Fair Trade Campaign.

Center for Global Education*

Augsburg College
731 21st. Ave. S.
Minneapolis, MN 55454
Phone: (612) 330-1159
Fax: (612) 330-1695
Contact: Janet Mathison, Director

DESCRIPTION

The center promotes experiential education, helping people expand their world view and deepen their understanding of international issues through international travel seminars, undergraduate semesters abroad, and faculty-development programs.

ACTIVITIES

The center arranges travel seminars to Mexico, Central America, and other parts of the world where participants meet with representatives in government and business as well as church and grassroots communities. Seminar participants are empowered to learn, teach, and work for social change. Some travel seminars attempt to sensitize teachers, especially those working with Latino immigrant students, to the specific economic, cultural, and legal issues surrounding immigration. Each year the center sponsors a semester-long program in Cuernavaca, Mexico, providing an introduction to the U.S.-Mexico border situation, an analysis of contemporary issues in Mexico and Central America, intensive Spanish study, living settings with Mexican families, and a two-week trip to Central America.

RESOURCES

- *Global Perspectives*. Free quarterly newsletter.

Chicanos Against Military Intervention in Latin America (CAMILA)*

PO Box 28083
San Antonio, TX 78228
Phone: (210) 229-6750
Contact: Antonio Cabral

DESCRIPTION

CAMILA seeks to foster increased understanding and solidarity between Mexico and the United States at the grassroots level. Its Committee for Democracy in Mexico attempts to arouse U.S. public opinion to the need for political reform in Mexico.

ACTIVITIES

CAMILA sponsors public-education forums showing videos on Latin America (Central America and Mexico in particular), speakers' forums featuring grassroots leaders from Mexico and other countries, and trips by U.S. activists to experience firsthand the situation in Mexico. It also provides information on Mexico's social, economic, and political movements to other activist groups in San Antonio, Texas.

RESOURCES

- *Mexico Notes*. A monthly newsletter.

Coalition for Fair Trade and Economic Justice*

c/o AFL-CIO Regional Office
611 S. Shatto Place #400
Los Angeles, CA 90005
Phone: (213) 387-1974
Fax: (213) 387-3525
Contact: Victor Muñoz

DESCRIPTION

The coalition attempts to rally opposition to NAFTA through education regarding its potentially negative impacts.

Development Group for Alternative Policies (GAP)*

927 15th St. NW #4
Washington, DC 20005
Phone: (202) 898-1566
Fax: (202) 898-1612
Email: (PeaceNet) dgap@igc.apc.org
Contact: Karen Hansen-Kuhn

DESCRIPTION

This nonprofit, international, development-policy group attempts to inject local perspectives from the countries of the South into policymaking circles in the North. It focuses on economic issues including structural adjustment, trade, and foreign assistance.

ACTIVITIES

Its NAFTA Information System is a resource for activist groups dealing with NAFTA.

LINKS

Development GAP is a founding member of MODTLE and also works with the Citizen Trade Watch Campaign. It maintains active cross-border links both with the Canadian networks and with RMALC and Equipo Pueblo in Mexico.

RESOURCES

- *Look Before You Leap: What You Should Know About a North American Free Trade Agreement*. Report in English and Spanish published in consultation with MODTLE, Citizen Trade Watch Campaign, Common Frontiers (Canada), and Equipo Pueblo (Mexico). Cost depends on number ordered.
- *NAFTATHOUGHTS*. Bimonthly newsletter. Available through PeaceNet or by mail upon request. Free.
- *Working Propositions for Zacatecas: Elements of an Alternative Approach to North American Development and Trade*. Action Canada Network, 1991.
- *Proposals from the Mexican Action Network on the Free Trade Agreement*. RMALC, 1991.
- *Final Declaration from the Zacatecas Forum*. 1991.
- *Citizen Trade Watch Campaign Factsheet on Waxman/Gephardt Resolution*, 1991.

Institute for Agriculture and Trade Policy (IATP)*

1313 5th St. SE #303
Minneapolis, MN 55414-1546
Phone: (612) 379-5980
Fax: (612) 379-5982
Email: (EcoNet) iatp
Contact: Michelle Thom

DESCRIPTION

IATP is a nonprofit research and education organization dedicated to creating environmentally and economically sustainable communities and regions through sound agriculture and trade policy. The institute assists public-interest organizations in effectively influencing both domestic and international policymaking by: 1) monitoring world events related to agriculture, the environment, community economic development, and trade; 2) analyzing these events regarding their potential economic or ecological impacts; 3) researching policy options to respond to these impacts; 4) preparing educational materials for distribution to policymakers and the general public; 5) providing staff and leadership training through seminars or on-site consultation; and 6) building national and international coalitions through conferences, study tours, action campaigns, and electronic bulletin boards. In 1988-89, the institute focused on GATT and the U.S.-Canada Free Trade Agreement. In 1990, IATP concerned itself with the trade aspects of the U.S. federal farm bill, the NAFTA negotiations, and preparations for the 1992 United Nations Conference on Environment and Development (UNCED).

ACTIVITIES

IATP promotes citizen dialogue on the effects of a free trade agreement through conferences with environmental and agricultural groups. Conference topics include potential links between free trade and the degradation of the environment, workers rights, human rights, and job security.

RESOURCES

- "An Injury to One is Un Agravio a Todos: The Need for a Mexico-U.S. Health and Safety Movement," by Matt Witt, in *New Solutions: A Journal of Environmental and Occupational Health Policy*, Winter 1991. 4 pages. $1.
- "Breaking into the Mexican Market: Policy Shifts Offer New Opportunities," by the U.S. Department of Agriculture and Foreign Agricultural Service, in *AgExporter*, March 1991. 23 pages. $1.
- *Free Trade vs. Sustainable Agriculture: Impact of U.S. Agriculture*, by Mark Ritchie. January 1991. 15 pages. $2.50
- *Press Advisory Packet*. Issued by citizen's groups warning of potential consequences of U.S.-Mexico-Canada free trade agreement. February 1991. 24 pages. $3.
- *Selling Canada's Environment Short: The Environmental Case Against the Trade Deal*, by the Canadian Environmental Law Association, 1989. 26 pages. $3.50.
- *Selling the Environment Short: An Environmental Assessment of the First Two Years of Free Trade Between Canada and the United States*, by Steven Shrybman, for the Canadian Environmental Law Association, November 1990. 22 pages. $3.
- "Selling the Environment Short: The U.S.-Canadian Free Trade Agreement—One Year Later," by Steven Shrybman. *Earth Island Journal*, Spring 1991. 3 pages. $1.
- *Statement of Mark A. Anderson, International Economist, AFL-CIO, Before the Sub-Committee on Trade, Committee on Ways and Means of the U.S. House of Representatives on U.S.-Mexico Economic Relations*, June 1990. 13 pages. $2.

- *Statement of Thomas R. Donahue, AFL-CIO, Before the U.S. Senate Finance Committee on the Proposed U.S.-Mexico Free Trade Agreement*, February 1991. 23 pages. $3.
- *The Consumer and Environmental Case Against Fast Track*, by Lori Wallach and Tom Hilliard for Public Citizen's Congress Watch. May 1991. 41 pages. $5.
- *The Continental Development and Trade Initiative: A Statement by Cuauhtémoc Cárdenas*. New York, February 1991. 8 pages. $1.
- *The Pro-Canada Dossier*, a production of the Pro-Canada Network (Action Canada Network). Looks at Canadian life two years after the signing of the free trade agreement with the United States, January-February 1991.
- *The U.S.-Canada Free Trade Agreement: Discussion of Its Potential Effects Upon U.S. and Canadian Agriculture and its Relationship with the Current Round of GATT Negotiations*, by Alex McKinney. 26 pages. $3.50.
- *U.S.-Mexico Free Trade: Opening Up the Debate*. Public forum on agricultural, environmental, and labor issues, January 1991. 31 pages. $4.
- *What Alternative Might There Be to a Mexico-U.S.-Canada Agreement?*, by William McGaughey. January 1991. 24 pages. $3.
- *What's The Big Deal: Some Straightforward Questions and Answers on Free Trade*, by the Pro-Canada Network.
- *Why the U.S. Should Oppose Free Trade with Mexico for Fruits and Vegetables*, by the Florida Fruit and Vegetable Association. November 1990. 9 pages. $1.50

Institute for Food and Development Policy (Food First)*

145 9th St.
San Francisco, CA 94103
Phone: (415) 864-8555
Fax: (415) 864-3909
Email: igc:foodfirst
Contact: John Gershman

DESCRIPTION

Food First is a nonprofit research and education-for-action center focusing on issues of hunger, poverty, environmental degradation, and development. It attempts to devise alternative strategies for participatory, equitable, and sustainable development.

ACTIVITIES

Building Alternatives to Free Trade in the Americas is a popularly accessible, information-dissemination project analyzing the impact of economic restructuring and free trade in Mexico, the United States, and Canada.

RESOURCES

- *Trading Freedom: How Free Trade Affects Our Lives, Work, and Environment*, by John Cavanagh, John Gershman, Karen Baker, and Gretchen Helmke, editors. Co-edited with the Institute for Policy Studies, this book critiques NAFTA and outlines a sustainable, participatory, and equitable alternative. $10 plus $3.50 postage in the U.S., $5 postage international.
- *Food First News*. No. 45, Fall 1991, includes an article about the myths and realities of free trade.

Institute for Policy Studies (IPS)*

1601 Connecticut Ave. NW #5
Washington, DC 20009
Phone: (202) 234-9382
Fax: (202) 387-7915
Contact: John Cavanagh

ACTIVITIES

Undertaking to devise alternative domestic and foreign policies, IPS takes a three-pronged approach: 1) educational workshops, upon request, to help other organizations understand basic issues (e.g. NAFTA); 2) policy development, whereby alternative policies are researched and published; and 3) networking.

LINKS

IPS is an active member (and co-founder) of MODTLE.

RESOURCES

- *Global Communities*. Quarterly newsletter. $15/yr.
- *Trading Freedom: How Free Trade Affects Our Lives, Work, and Environment*, by John Cavanagh, John Gershman, Karen Baker, and Gretchen Helmke, editors. Co-edited with the Institute for Food and Development Policy. 130 pages. $10 plus postage.

Interfaith Center on Corporate Responsibility (ICCR)*

475 Riverside Dr. #566
New York, NY 10115-0050
Phone: (212) 870-2984
Fax: (212) 870-2023
Contact: Marcia Osgood

DESCRIPTION

This North American coalition of nearly 250 Protestant and Roman Catholic institutional investors (including denominations, religious communities, agencies, pension funds, dioceses, and health care corporations) utilizes church investments and other resources to promote change in unjust or harmful corporate policies and practices, challenging the powerful role corporations play in the use and misuse of the earth's human and physical resources. ICCR member organizations also make alternative investments to promote economic justice and development in low-income and minority communities.

LINKS

ICCR is an active member of the Coalition for Justice in the Maquiladoras.

RESOURCES

- *The Corporate Examiner*. A publication examining the policies and practices of major U.S. corporations regarding apartheid, star wars, nuclear weapons, minorities, women, alternative investments, energy, the environment, and international marketing. Published ten times yearly. $35/yr.

International Student, Trade, Environment and Development Program (INSTEAD)*

PO Box 13208, Dinkytown Station
Minneapolis, MN 55414
Phone: (612) 379-3905
Fax: (612) 379-5982
Email: (EcoNet) instead
Contact: J Burger

DESCRIPTION

INSTEAD works with students and youth groups focusing on trade, environment, and development issues. Its organizers facilitate the involvement of concerned youth organizations in local coalition efforts aimed at addressing the link between ecology and economics. In its efforts to bring the perspective of youth to ecological and economic issues, INSTEAD hopes to insure that young people continue as members of local coalitions and networks working on international concerns.

ACTIVITIES

A speakers bureau links student and youth groups with resource people able to explain the linkages between international trade, the environment, and development issues. Speakers include nongovernmental representatives, students, and experienced organizers/activists. INSTEAD promotes regional student conferences on organizing skills related to key international issues involving trade, the environment, and development. It also convenes trinational meetings between students in Mexico, Canada, and the United States promoting discussions, planning, and actions regarding NAFTA and the 500 Years of Resistance events.

RESOURCES

- Educational materials for use by student and youth groups. Topics include NAFTA, GATT, quincentennial, etc.
- Up-to-the-minute information via electronic networks EcoNet and InterNet for cooperating student and youth organizations. Participating groups receive articles, news, and analysis about international issues.

Mexican American State Legislators Policy Institute (MASLPI)*

1410 Grant St. #C-306
Denver, CO 80203
Phone: (303) 860-8935
Fax: (303) 860-0472
Contact: Patrick S. Sanchez, Executive Director

DESCRIPTION

MASLPI is a network of Hispanic State Legislators in the Southwest that analyzes policy decisions and legislative actions that impact on Mexican American, other Hispanic, and minority populations in the region.

ACTIVITIES

MASLPI examines the impact of NAFTA on border states in order to determine legislation needed to insure protection of the environment, rights of workers, health, etc.

RESOURCES

- *MASLPI Network*. Quarterly newsletter. $20/yr. for nonmembers.

Mexico Communications

PO Box 1707
El Paso, TX 79949
Phone: (915) 533-5271
Contact: Lourdes McClinton, Editor

RESOURCES

- *In-Bond Maquiladora Directory*. Updated, July 1992.

Mexico Resource Center*

PO Box 7547
Austin, TX 78713
Phone: (512) 478-3065
Contact: Philip Russell

DESCRIPTION

This group compiles information about Mexico (concentrating on such topics as the 1988 Mexican elections, current politics, human rights, and free trade) and disseminates it through a library and a speakers service.

RESOURCES

- *Mexico Biannual*. Summary of current events in Mexico. $9.95
- *Mexico Periodical Index*. Annual index of major magazines. $9.95

Mexico-U.S. Dialogos*

103 Washington St. #8
New York, NY 10006
Phone: (212) 233-0155
Fax: (212) 233-0238
Contact: David Brooks

DESCRIPTION

The Dialogos program is designed to promote a broad, binational dialogue among social constituencies directly affected by the economic integration process, with the objective of forging alliances among those sectors. Its projects are a combination of people-to-people organizing, research, and education. Dialogos coordinates bi/trinational conferences, seminars, speaking tours, and media projects.

ACTIVITIES

Popular Perspectives Project. Since 1988, Dialogos has coordinated a series of binational exchanges. The meetings are entirely defined by the participants, which include labor unions, farm workers, environmentalists, Latino and African-American organizations, immigrant-rights groups, and policy analysts. Participants identify common concerns, explore elements for a shared agenda vis-à-vis binational relations, and initiate cooperative projects.

Educational Resource Project. Dialogos is compiling an educational resource packet on contemporary Mexico for use by academic institutions as well as religious, labor, and community groups. This two-week seminar packet introduces students to the complex culture of Mexico, acquaints them with key issues in Mexico today, and explores current themes in U.S.-Mexico relations.

Binational Labor Project. This project facilitates communication between labor unions in Mexico and those in the United States both by providing resources on critical economic and political issues, and by arranging binational research exchanges. During these labor tours, U.S. trade unionists visit key industrial plants and *maquiladoras* in Mexico and meet with their Mexican counterparts, while representatives of Mexican labor visit U.S. workers affected by runaway shops and economic integration with Mexico.

New Viewpoints Project. Dialogos perceives that Mexican perspectives on the intensifying debate about U.S.-Mexico relations and hemispheric affairs are drastically underrepresented in the United States, and at the same time alternative trading suggestions developed by nongovernmental, U.S. groups are not being heard by the Mexican public. The New Viewpoints Project helps to remedy this situation in the United States by: sponsoring forums on Mexico (often coordinated with other U.S. organizations); facilitating coverage of leading Mexican social and political analysts in U.S. media; hosting Mexican delegations (e.g. of human rights activists, political cartoonists, urban organizers, etc.) that offer insight into the social and political complexities of Mexico; and disseminating resources to the media. In Mexico, Dialogos facilitates communication by: introducing North American viewpoints on U.S. social concerns into national daily newspapers, journals, and academic publications as well as popular forums; sponsoring meetings between Mexican social organizations and their U.S. counterparts; and providing research assistance on the United States to Mexican media, policy institutes, universities, and grassroots organizations.

LINKS

In Mexico, Dialogos works closely with the RMALC, Fundación Lázaro Cárdenas, Instituto de Estudios para el Desarrollo Rural "Maya," Equipo Pueblo, Asamblea de Barrios, and other organizations.

Minnesota Lawyers International Human Rights Committee*

400 Second Ave. S. #1050
Minneapolis, MN 55401
Phone: (612) 341-3302
Fax: (612) 341-2971
Contact: Daniel L. Gerdts

DESCRIPTION

This private, nongovernmental organization of lawyers, concerned citizens, and jurists advocates against individual human rights abuses, researches and investigates human rights conditions in other countries, encourages the adoption of international human rights standards by all countries, and educates its members, the bar, political leaders, and the public about human rights issues. The Minnesota Lawyers Committee is one of the three nongovernmental, international human rights monitors working in Mexico (the others being Americas Watch and Amnesty International).

ACTIVITIES

In 1988 the Minnesota Lawyers Committee began sending fact-finding missions to U.S.-Mexico border cities and to Mexico City to interview human rights workers, journalists, lawyers, and union leaders in order to investigate human rights abuses, especially reports of torture and abuse of authority by the Mexican judicial police.

LINKS

The Committee works with Comisión de Solidaridad y Defensa de los Derechos Humanos (COSYDDHAC) (Human Rights Solidarity and Defense Commission), based in the Mexican state of Chihuahua, and with the other Mexican nongovernmental human rights organizations.

RESOURCES

- *Paper Protection: Human Rights Violations and the Mexican Criminal Justice System.* Report. July 1990. $7.
- *The Homicide of Dr. Victor Manuel Oropeza. A Case Study of Failed Human Rights Reforms in Mexico*. Report. December 1991. $5.

National Coalition of Education Activists

1247 E. Burleigh St.
Milwaukee, WI 53212
Phone: (414) 265-6217
Fax: (414) 272-1232
Contact: Bob Peterson

DESCRIPTION

A coalition of community activists and local leaders from the National Education Association, American Federation of Teachers, and independent unions.

ACTIVITIES

The coalition organizes trips by Mexican teachers to the United States in order to discuss: the impact of free trade and economic integration on public services and public workers; ways of building worker-community alliances; bilingual education; union democracy; and the need to reexamine teaching methods and content in order to develop critical thinking by students.

National Council of La Raza (NCLR)*

810 1st St. NE #300
Washington, DC 20002
Phone: (202) 289-1380
Fax: (202) 289-8173
Contact: Cecilia Muñoz

DESCRIPTION

La Raza is a nonpartisan organization with 150 affiliates advocating for Hispanic interests. It relates to NAFTA through policy formation and coalition building.

RESOURCES

- *Agenda*. Quarterly newsletter. Free.

National Network for Immigrant and Refugee Rights (NNIRR)*

310 8th St. #307
Oakland, CA 94607
Phone: (415) 465-1984
Contact: Cathi Tactaquin, Director

DESCRIPTION

This organization champions the rights of immigrants and refugees by strengthening national educational efforts, communication, and coordination among advocates and organizers around the country. Its members include community, church, labor, and legal groups.

ACTIVITIES

NNIRR functions as a clearinghouse of information and resources, organizes national conferences and meetings, and promotes immigrant and refugee rights through the media.

RESOURCES

- *Network News*. Bimonthly newsletter. $10-20 for individuals, $25 for institutions, $5 for fixed income/unemployed persons.
- Member's bulletin, informational mailings, and action alerts for NNIRR members.

North American Congress on Latin America (NACLA)*

475 Riverside Dr. #454
New York, NY 10115
Phone: (212) 870-3146
Contact: Susan Y. Wood

DESCRIPTION

An independent, nonprofit organization founded in 1966 to research the political economy of the Americas. Its publication *Report of the Americas* is the largest circulating English-language magazine on the Americas, with readers in over 70 countries.

RESOURCES

- *NACLA Report of the Americas*. Five issues per year. Of special interest is *The New Gospel: North American Free Trade*, Vol. 24, #6, May 1991. Subscriptions in the U.S.: $22/yr. for individuals, $40/yr. for institutions. Overseas: $32/yr. for individuals, $50/yr. for institutions. Back issues: $4 plus $1 postage and handling.

South and Meso American Indian Information Center (SAIIC)*

PO Box 28703
Oakland, CA 94604
Phone: (510) 834-4263
Fax: (510) 834-4264
Email: (PeaceNet) saiic@igc.org.
Contact: Nilo Cayuqueo, Coordinator

DESCRIPTION

SAIIC facilitates exchanges and direct communication between the indigenous peoples of Canada, the United States, Meso (Mexico, Central America, and the Caribbean), and South America.

ACTIVITIES

The center has three ongoing programs. The Information and Networking Program consists of educational multimedia presentations for the public, networking with community groups, schools, church groups, and public institutions. This program establishes ongoing ties with native and non-native organizations to mobilize needed action in support of Indians in South and Meso America. The Visitor Program transports leaders from South and Meso American Indian communities in order to meet with native people of the United States and Canada. Contacts are also established with environmental and human rights organizations, policy institutions, and foundations. The Women's Project offers resources and technical training to Indian women in Meso and South America. The Women's Project is helping to build an international Indian women's network, and distributes proceedings of international women's conferences.

RESOURCES

- *SAIIC Newsletter*. Quarterly journal. $15/yr. for individuals, $25 for institutions.
- *The First Continental Conference on 500 Years of Indian Resistance, Quito, Ecuador*. Goals and perspectives of the Commissions on Women, Self-Determination, 500 Years of Resistance, Education, Culture and Religion, Territory and Natural Resources, Indigenous Law, Human Rights and Political Prisoners, and Nonindigenous Solidarity. $5.
- *Video of the Quito Conference*. $25. Also available for rent.
- *500 Years of Resistance, Resources for Action Packet*. A comprehensive listing of over 600 native and non-native organizations from South, Central, and North America, as well as Europe working on alternative quincentennial events, Indian solidarity, and the struggle for indigenous rights. $10 plus $2 for shipping; International: $14.

Southwest Organizing Project (SWOP)*

211 10th St. SW
Albuquerque, NM 87102
Phone: (505) 247-8832
Fax: (505) 247-9972
Contact: Richard Moore

DESCRIPTION

SWOP is a multiracial, multi-issue, grassroots-membership community organization that fights for basic rights to land and resources, the growth and preservation of minority cultures, and self-determination. It focuses on developing leadership in minority and working-class neighborhoods (with a special focus on women and youth) in order to combat racism, sexism, and age and social-class discrimination.

ACTIVITIES

SWOP founded the Southwest Network for Environmental and Economic Justice, an effort to broaden regional strategies and perspectives on social and economic justice, racial, and environmental issues.

LINKS

SWOP is member of the Coalition for Justice in the Maquiladoras.

RESOURCES

- *Voces Unidas*. Quarterly newsletter. $25/yr.

Southwest Voter Research Institute (SVRI)*

403 East Commerce #260
San Antonio, TX 78205
Phone: (210) 222-8014
Fax: (210) 222-8474
Contact: Andrew Fernandez, President

DESCRIPTION

SVRI is a nonprofit, nonpartisan organization chartered to conduct research that may be used to improve the level of political participation in Hispanic communities. Its objectives are: to provide current political and demographic baseline data by precinct for voter-registration campaigns; to inform the Hispanic leadership and public about the political opinions and behavior of Hispanics; to provide support to lawsuits challenging discriminatory election practices and systems; to provide ongoing evaluation of voter-mobilization strategies; and to inform the Hispanic leadership and public about the impact of public policies like NAFTA on Hispanics.

ACTIVITIES

SVRI's Latin America Project—through a program of training sessions, delegations, seminars, polls, and publications—develops a large group of Hispanic leaders articulate in the key issues of U.S.-Latin American relations.

RESOURCES

- *Mexico Infopak* (see p. 166).
- *Latin America Project Reports*. Studies on U.S. policy in Latin America.

OTHER OFFICES

Southwest Voter Research Institute (SVRI)
1712 W. Beverly Blvd. #203
Montebello, CA 90640
Phone: (213) 728-2706
Fax: (213) 728-4001
Contact: Antonio González

Third World Resources*

Data Center
464 19th St.
Oakland, CA 94612-2297
Phone: (415) 835-4692/536-1876
Fax: (415) 835-3017
Email: (PeaceNet) tfenton or (GeoNet) geo2:tfenton
Contact: Tom Fenton/Mary Heffron

DESCRIPTION

This financially independent affiliate of the Data Center identifies, collects, evaluates, and publicizes print and audiovisual resources on third world regions and issues. It then compiles this information and produces geographical directories with annotated descriptions of organizations and resources.

RESOURCES

- *Quarterly Review*. A 24-page newsletter of resources from and about the third world.
- Documentation Clearinghouse of the nation's most comprehensive, up-to-date, and accessible library collections of print resources on the full range of third world regions and issues. The clearinghouse distributes its information through PeaceNet and through the ERIC Clearinghouse on Social Studies Education. A library and a news-clipping service are also available from the Data Center (same address and phone number; email: [PeaceNet] datacenter, contact: Fred Goff, Executive Director).

U.S.-Mexico Free Trade Reporter*

1725 K St. NW #200
Washington, DC 20006
Phone: (202) 785-8658/8595
Fax: (202) 785-8589
Contact: George H. Lesser

RESOURCES

- *U.S.-Mexico Free Trade Reporter*. A biweekly newsletter on trade, investment and related transborder issues, with editors in both Washington, DC, and Mexico City.

Washington Office on Latin America (WOLA)*

110 Maryland Ave. NE #404
Washington, DC 20002-5696
Phone: (202) 544-8045
Fax: (202) 546-5288
Contact: Jared Kotler, Associate for Central America and Mexico

DESCRIPTION

WOLA informs U.S. policymakers about conditions in Latin America, advocating a just and humane U.S. foreign policy. It also educates collegial groups in Latin America, and interacts with U.S. religious and nongovernmental organizations as part of the Washington human rights community.

ACTIVITIES

As part of its effort to initiate programs on Mexico, WOLA hosted a workshop on human rights and the free trade agreement, in which Mexican, Canadian, and U.S. human rights activists participated.

RESOURCES

- *Enlace*. Quarterly, in Spanish. Distributed mainly to Latin American collegial organizations.

Women's Alternative Economics Network (WAEN)

1405 E. 3rd St.
Winston-Salem, NC 27101
Phone: (919) 370-4330
Contact: Anne Lennon

DESCRIPTION

These women from diverse regions and organizations in the United States are interested in searching for new economic alternatives to overcome poverty and attain a higher standard of living.

ACTIVITIES

In November 1991, WAEN convened a binational forum at the headquarters of La Mujer Obrera in El Paso, Texas.

World Policy Institute*

777 United Nations Plaza
New York, NY 10017
Phone: (212) 490-0010
Fax: (212) 986-1482
Contact: Richard Caplan, Acting Director

DESCRIPTION

An affiliate of the New School for Social Research, the World Policy Institute is an educational organization engaged in the formulation and promotion of public-policy recommendations relating to U.S. and international economic and security issues. Policy research for the institute is conducted by a network of experts, including independent analysts and specialists from academia, business, and government, as well as fellows of the World Policy Institute. As an institute, it does not have a specific position on NAFTA, but has offered critical comments on early drafts.

ACTIVITIES

The Mexico Project is devoted to monitoring the development of human rights and democracy in Mexico, assessing the implications of these trends for North American economic integration, and evaluating the effects of U.S. policies toward Mexico. Through the World Policy Lecture Series, leading analysts address current topics in international affairs at the New School for Social Research in New York.

RESOURCES

- *World Policy Journal*. Quarterly. Discussion of U.S. foreign policy and international affairs. $23/yr. for individuals, $30/yr. for institutions.

PART V

Academic Institutions

INTRODUCTION

The academic community is the source of many insights and materials regarding the process of integration now under way in North America. Until the late 1980s, most scholarly research in the three countries concentrated on binational social, political, and cultural relationships. As Canada and the United States moved toward a free trade accord in 1989, however, research on economic relations surged among the two nations' scholars. At the same time, cross-border links among members of each country's academic community began multiplying at a rapid pace.

This same pattern is being played out alongside the NAFTA negotiations and the trinational economic integration they symbolize. Concern about the socioeconomic effects of integration sparked a sharp increase in the number of academic centers and research groups in all three countries. This upsurge has been most pronounced in Mexico. Scholars in that country are studying the effects of new trade and investment ties with Canada and the United States. Moreover, as Mexico and the United States become more interdependent, Mexican academics are analyzing U.S. influence on Mexican society, politics, and the economy.

In all three countries, cross-border linkages among academic institutions are being created where once they did not exist. These relations are most numerous between U.S. institutions and their counterparts in Canada and Mexico. But interactions among scholars in Mexico and Canada are growing, stimulated by their common need to protect their own national interests in the face of the overwhelming power of the United States.

These links often take the form of conferences and forums that bring together representatives from the three nations in an academic setting. Enriched by these transnational ties, academics have a distinct advantage over other social sectors—such as base communities and nongovernmental organizations—that have only just begun to establish trilateral relations. Academics interested in the study of U.S.-Mexico border relations, for instance, have participated in transborder networks for more than a decade.

Even with the creation of new projects and transnational linkages, academic institutions are not as influential in the formation of official policy as one might guess, although this varies from country to country. Canadian institutions are the most isolated from policymakers, while certain U.S. think tanks and Mexican universities are privy to insider consultations and policy influence with their respective administrations.

Scholars do, however, often have a role in shaping public opinion and their research is sometimes used by policymakers to justify their stands on political and economic issues. An interesting example of this phenomenon concerns Mexican academics critical of free trade. Due to their prominence in important sectors in the United States, many of these scholars are publishing articles about free trade in major U.S. newspapers like the *Los Angeles Times*. The views they express in those forums are often filtered back into Mexico. In this way, these academics are able to focus national attention and stimulate political debate in their own country on the issue of free trade.

This section focuses on two types of academic institutions: those affiliated with universities, and think tanks that analyze issues and design policies for government, business, or social justice groups. Academic institutions that actually participate in political or social campaigns, or that serve on the staffs or governing boards of popular-organizing networks, are listed under Advocacy Organizations or in the appropriate section of the directory.

We have chosen to include only those centers and think tanks with a long-term institutional interest in bi- or trinational issues. This means we have excluded many top-notch scholars whose related work may be very important. We suggest that people interested in a given topic use the following resources as a guide to the larger body of academic work being done on North American integration:

1) **Latin American Studies Association**

William Pitt Union
Room 946
University of Pittsburgh
Pittsburgh, PA 15260
Phone: (412) 648-7929
Fax: (412) 624-7145
Email: (Bitnet) lasa@pittvms
The list of papers presented at LASA conferences provide valuable leads to current research in the field.

2) **PROFMEX**, listed below, has dozens of affiliates in the three countries that should be able to provide materials and contacts on specific topics.

3) **Center for U.S.-Mexican Studies**, also listed in this section, publishes an International Guide to Research on Mexico every two years.

1. CANADA

C.D. Howe Institute*

125 Adelaide St. E.
Toronto, ON M5C 1L7
Phone: (416) 865-1904
Fax: (416) 865-1866
Contact: Adam H. Zimmerman, Chairman, or Thomas E. Kierans, President and Chief Executive Officer

DESCRIPTION

C.D. Howe is an independent, nonprofit research and educational institution. Its goals are to identify current and emerging issues of economic and social policy facing Canadians; to analyze response options for the public and private sectors; to recommend appropriate, policy options that in the institute's view, best serve the national interest; and to communicate the conclusions of its research to a domestic and international audience in a clear, nonpartisan way. The institute was created by a merger of the Private Planning Association of Canada (PPAC) and the C.D. Howe Memorial Foundation.

OTHER OFFICES

C.D. Howe Institute
PO Box 1621, Station M
Calgary, AB T2P 2L7
Phone: (403) 233-8044

Canadian Centre for Policy Alternatives (CCPA)*

251 Laurier Ave. W. #804
Ottawa, ON K1P 5J6
Phone: (613) 563-1341
Fax: (613) 233-1458
Contact: Sandra Sorensen, Executive Director

DESCRIPTION

The centre is committed to research and analysis on economic and social issues that reflect the concerns of women and men; labor and business; churches, cooperatives and voluntary agencies as well as governments; minorities and disadvantaged people as well as fortunate individuals.

ACTIVITIES

The CCPA publishes research reports, sponsors conferences, organizes briefings, and provides informed comment on the issues of the day from a nonpartisan perspective.

LINKS

On some issues, CCPA research relates directly to the outreach program of the Action Canada Network.

RESOURCES

- *Going South: Cheap Labour as an Unfair Subsidy in North American Free Trade*, by Jim Stanford. $8 for members, $12 for nonmembers, $20 for institutions.
- *North American Free Trade: A Critical Economic Perspective*, by Ricardo Grinspun. 21 pages. $8 for members, $12 for nonmembers, $20 for institutions.
- *Hard Lessons: Living with Free Trade*, by Bruce Campbell. Documents the Canadian experience and includes a detailed explanation of how the free trade agreement works. 25 pages. $8 for members, $12 for nonmembers, $20 for institutions.
- *Continental Trade Alert*, by the Canadian Centre for Policy Alternatives, the Action Canada Network, and Common Frontiers. Periodic information sheet. Free.
- *Paying the Price: How Free Trade is Hurting the Environment, Regional Development and Canadian and Mexican Workers*. Three research studies in one report: *Selling the Environment Short*, by Steven Shrybman; *Free Trade and Regional Development Policy*, by Scott Sinclair; *The Mexican Connection*, by the Latin American Working Group. 29 pages. $8 for members, $12 for nonmembers, $20 for institutions.
- *Free Trade and Workers' Rights: The European Social Charter*, by Matthew Sanger. 18 pages. $8 for members, $12 for nonmembers, $20 for institutions.
- *Health Care as a Business: The Legacy of Free Trade*, by Pat Armstrong and Hugh Armstrong. 24 pages. $8 for members, $12 for nonmembers, $20 for institutions.
- *Ten Reasons why Canada Should not Enter into a Trilateral Free Trade Agreement with the United States and Mexico*, by Bruce Campbell. Pamphlet. $1 for members, $2 for nonmembers and institutions.
- *Fast Track, Fast Shuffle: The Economic Consequences of the Proposed Trade Agreement with Mexico*, by Jeff Faux and Richard Rothstein, Economic Policy Institute. 25 pages. $8 for members, $12 for nonmembers, $20 for institutions.
- *Alternatives to Free Trade*, edited by Mel Watkins. Three research studies in one report: *Natural Resources and the Canada-U.S. Free Trade Agreement*, by Thomas Gunton; *The Mulroney-Reagan Accord in a Global Perspective*, by Morris Miller; *Canadian Industry and the Free Trade Agreement*, by Manfred Bienefeld. 48 pages. $8 for members, $12 for nonmembers, $20 for institutions.
- *Job Losses in Canadian Manufacturing, 1989-91*, by Andrew Jackson. 5 pages. Free.

Centre for International Studies (CIS)

University of Toronto
18 Madison Ave.
Toronto, ON M5R 2S1
Phone: (416) 978-3350
Fax: (416) 978-2910
Contact: Leonard Waverman

DESCRIPTION

This nonpartisan, interdisciplinary research center, focusing on the political, legal, and economic relationship between sovereign states, serves as a link between Canadian scholars and their counterparts in other countries. The formal mission of the CIS is to examine Canada-U.S.-Mexican relations; to analyze the major underlying forces shaping the international economy; to explore the linkages between these trends and government policies in an international policy framework; and to suggest policy options necessary to promote the private sector as a key ingredient for sustained growth.

ACTIVITIES

Through the Visiting Chair Program, senior academics from North America, Europe, and the Pacific Rim meet and participate in CIS's research. In Toronto in November 1991, CIS and the Fraser Institute organized a conference entitled "How Free Trade is Progressing."

Centre for Research on Latin America and the Caribbean (CERLAC)*

York University, Founders College
4700 Keele St.
North York, ON M3J 1P3
Phone: (416) 736-5237
Fax: (416) 736-5735
Email: cerlac@yorkvm1.netnorth

DESCRIPTION

CERLAC is an interdisciplinary research unit concerned with the economic development, political and social organization, and cultural contributions of Latin America and the Caribbean. The centre works to build academic and cultural links between these regions and Canada; to inform researchers, policy advisors, and the public on matters concerning the regions; and to assist in the development of research and teaching institutions that directly benefit the peoples of the regions.

ACTIVITIES

As part of its Mexico Program, CERLAC fellows and graduate students meet periodically with scholars from other Canadian institutions to discuss their research on Mexico. CERLAC sponsors conferences, lectures, public information services, and cultural activities and has been contracted to write reports for the Canadian government.

RESOURCES

- Documentation centre containing research on Latin America and the Caribbean.

Centre for Trade Policy and Law (CTPL)*

Norman Paterson School of International Affairs
Social Sciences Research Building #106
Carleton University
Ottawa, ON K1S 5B6
Phone: (613) 788-6696
Fax: (613) 788-3981
Contact: Murray G. Smith, Director, or Melanie Burston, Administrative Assistant

DESCRIPTION

Jointly sponsored by the Normal Paterson School of International Affairs at Carleton University and the Faculty of Law at the University of Ottawa, the CTPL was established to promote greater public understanding of trade-policy issues, to foster independent analysis and research of trade issues, and to encourage the development of trade-policy professionals.

ACTIVITIES

CTPL's resources are dedicated to teaching graduate and professional students at the two sponsoring universities and to programs for government staff, business, and labor organizations. It develops teaching programs and materials, encourages faculty interchanges, and hosts periodic seminars and conferences on the teaching of trade policy in Canada.

RESOURCES

- A central repository for material on trade policy.

Fraser Institute*

626 Bute St.
Vancouver, BC V6E 3M1
Phone: (604) 688-0221
Fax: (604) 688-8539
Contact: Dr. Michael Walker, Executive Director

DESCRIPTION

This conservative economic, social research, and educational organization directs public attention to the value of competitive markets and the role they can play in solving Canada's economic and social problems.

ACTIVITIES

The institute is home to the North America 20/20 Project on Free Trade in the Americas. It operates an active event and conference program, a campaign to write editorials that are printed in daily and weekly newspapers and magazines in Canada explaining the merits of free trade, a National Media Archive that maintains a database of national television news, and a center for comparative policy analysis that monitors economic and social-policy developments worldwide.

RESOURCES

- *Fraser Forum.* Monthly economic diary of editorial commentaries.
- *Continental Accord: North American Economic Integration.* Edited by Steven Globerman. Economic, social, and political issues surrounding North American integration. 1991. 174 pages. $19.95.
- *Negotiating and Implementing a North American Free Trade Agreement.* Edited by Leonard Waverman. 1992. 152 pages. $19.95.
- A set of papers presented at a November 1991 Toronto conference. Issues: free trade (in energy, in the financial sector, in the North American auto industry, in agriculture), investment policies (in Canada, the United States and Mexico), macroeconomic effects, impacts on medium-term employment and wages, intellectual property, tariffs, etc. $9.95 for each paper + 7% G.S.T. for Canadian residents, $3 for shipping and handling.

OTHER OFFICES

Fraser Institute
55 King St. W. #2550
Toronto, ON M5K 1E7
Phone: (416) 363-6575
Fax: (416) 367-1029

North-South Institute*

55 Murray St. #200
Ottawa, ON K1N 5M3
Phone: (613) 236-3535
Fax: (613) 237-7435
Contact: Ann Weston

DESCRIPTION

Through policy-relevant research, this independent, nonprofit, nonpartisan research institute promotes and encourages a greater understanding of the problems and opportunities of world development.

ACTIVITIES

The institute directs one project to analyze the social impact of NAFTA on Canada and Mexico, and a second project to examine how NAFTA affects trade diversion and trade creation in developing countries.

The Canada-Latin America Forum (FOCAL), an adjunct of the North-South Institute, was created in 1990 to accelerate partnering between various sectors in Canada and Latin America—ranging from business, political, and academic to cultural. FOCAL acts as a national clearinghouse, permitting improved access to information about hemispheric activities and research affecting Canada, and serving as a point of contact for the media, regional networks, and research groups. Contact: Juanita Montalvo. Phone: (613) 236-3535. Fax: (613) 789-9067.

RESOURCES

- *Social Subsidies and Trade with Developing Countries*. 37 pages. $6.
- *Trade Bargaining in Canada and the U.S.: Drifting Towards Regionalism?* 42 pages. $8.
- *Implications of a NAFTA for East Asian Developing Countries*. 22 pages. $5.
- *Free Trade with a Human Face: The Social Dimensions of the CUSFTA and the proposed NAFTA* (in progress, approx. 45 pages and $10).

Simon Fraser University

Department of Economics
Burnaby, BC V5A 1S6
Fax: (604) 291-5994
Contact: Richard D. Harris

ACTIVITIES

Professor Richard Harris has written several papers on economic integration in North and South America.

RESOURCES

- *Free Trade in the Americas: Some New Estimates of the Economic Impact*, by Richard Harris. 1991.

University of Calgary*

Faculty of Social Science
2500 University Dr. NW
Calgary, AB T2N 1N4
Phone: (403) 220-6418
Fax: (403) 289-8566
Contact: Stephen J. Randall, Chair in American Studies

DESCRIPTION

The University of Calgary boasts the largest number of Mexican specialists in Canada in a wide range of fields from Anthropology and Archeology through History, Political Science, Geography, Environmental Design, and Spanish. It also employs specialists on Canadian and U.S. foreign policy, trade policy, and economic development, and hosts an international center.

ACTIVITIES

The Department of Economics is developing an exchange program with Colegio de la Frontera Norte in Tijuana.

RESOURCES

- *North America Without Borders: Integrating Canada, the United States and Mexico*. Edited by Stephen J. Randall. University of Calgary Press, 1992.
- Canada Mexicanist Newsletter. Edited by Herman Konrad, Department of History/Anthropology and published biannually at the University of Calgary with the assistance of the Canadian Department of External Affairs.
- A study was recently completed for the Inter-American Development Bank and ECLAC on the petroleum industry and Western Hemisphere trade liberalization.

2. MEXICO

Asociación Nacional de Universidades e Institutos de Enseñanza Superior (ANUIES)

Insurgentes Sur 2133
Col. San Angel
México, D.F. 01000
Phone: (5) 5-50-63-99/48-85
Fax: (5) 5-50-48-57
Contact: Juan Casillas García León or Ermilo J. Marroquín

DESCRIPTION

The Mexican Association of Universities and Public Institutes of Higher Education (ANUIES) is the official representative of all Mexican universities. As such it works jointly with PROFMEX to coordinate both networks' binational activities.

ACTIVITIES

ANUIES participates in the Free Trade Agreement Advisory Board through four of its representatives: UNAM and UAM for the public universities, and the ITESM and ITAM for the private ones.

Centro de Análisis e Investigación Económica (CAIE)*

Instituto Tecnológico Autónomo de México (ITAM)
Av. Santa Teresa 930
Col. Héroes de Padierna
México, D.F. 10700
Phone: (5) 6-52-52-12
Fax: (5) 6-52-62-84
Contact: Dr. Manuel Sánchez G., Director

DESCRIPTION

ITAM is one of Mexico's top economic research institutions. Key economic policymakers like Treasury Secretary Pedro Aspe are alumni, and the school enjoys good access to the current administration. ITAM and its CAIE have a strong private-sector orientation, and strongly support NAFTA.

ACTIVITIES

CAIE develops macroeconomic and sectorial analysis, organizes conferences and seminars, and provides economic advice regarding the myriad perspectives concerning the Mexican economy.

LINKS

CAIE is an active participant in the Inter-American Bank Research Center Network.

RESOURCES

- *Informe Mensual sobre la Economía Mexicana*. Monthly analysis of the present economic situation, synthesis of recent research, economic indicators, forecasts, etc. U.S. $300/yr.
- *The Mexico Quarterly*. Analysis of Mexican economic reality. Published quarterly by Shearson Lehman Brothers, Inc.

Centro de Estudios de Estados Unidos

Instituto de Estudios Económicos y Regionales
Universidad de Guadalajara
Guadalajara, Jal.
Phone: (36) 24-28-03
Fax: (36) 23-37-94
Contact: Jesús Arroyo A., Center Director

DESCRIPTION

Centro de Estudios de Estados Unidos (Center of U.S. Studies) at the University of Guadalajara hosts a Mexico-U.S. project of collaborative, interdisciplinary research involving scholars and policymakers from Mexico and the United States focusing on long-term trends in Mexico's central-western region. The project has three main research components: 1) U.S.-Mexican economic relations and its impact in Mexico's western region; 2) economic growth, urbanization, and their ecological impacts; and 3) migration within the Mexican West and from the West to the United States. The program offers stipends to University of Guadalajara researchers to study U.S.-Mexican policy issues, and sponsors a series of working conferences of scholars and policymakers in order to debate policy recommendations. The expertise of its academic staff lies primarily in the areas of U.S.-Mexican relations and their impact in the Guadalajara region, and migration from the Guadalajara region to the United States.

LINKS

The university holds joint research meetings with the UCLA Program on Mexico.

Centro de Estudios Estratégicos (CEE)

Instituto Tecnológico de Estudios Superiores de Monterrey (ITESM)
Sucursal de Correos J
Monterrey, N.L. 64849
Phone: (83) 58-20-00 ext. 3901
Contact: Héctor Moreira

DESCRIPTION

Monterrey Tech (ITESM) is famous for its very strong private-sector orientation promoting free trade. Its Center for Strategic Studies (CEE) conducts research on Mexican-U.S. relations, regional development, and public-policy planning. The center analyzes differences between U.S. and Mexican negotiating styles and the adaptation problems of American executives and their families living in Mexico. Research is oriented toward enhancing the international competitiveness of the state of Nuevo León.

ACTIVITIES

CEE hosted a symposium in November 1991 in Monterrey on the Competitive Position of the North American Bloc (Mexico-United States-Canada).

RESOURCES

- *Estrategia*. Newsletter. Analyzes NAFTA and the Mexican exporting sector.
- Working papers on the manufacturing sector of the state of Nuevo León, the state's standard of living, and the exporting sector.

Centro de Investigaciones sobre Estados Unidos de América (CISEUA)*

Universidad Nacional Autónoma de México (UNAM)
Torre II de Humanidades, piso 11
Ciudad Universitaria
México, D.F. 04510
Phone: (5) 6-23-03-00/01
Fax: (5) 5-50-03-79
Contact: Mónica Verea Campos, Director

DESCRIPTION

UNAM is less an institution than an association of centers, CISEUA being one of the most prominent. CISEUA studies the United States, and Mexico-U.S. relations. One prominent member of CISEUA is the analyst Adolfo Aguilar Zinser (see p. 111).

ACTIVITIES

In January 1992 CISEUA participated in the binational event Mexico-United States: Energy, Environment, and the Free Trade Agreement.

LINKS

CISEUA is member of PROFMEX.

RESOURCES

- *Voices of Mexico*. Quarterly magazine, published by Ambassador Hugo B. Margain. Distributed by CISEUA-UNAM and by Books from Mexico, PO Box 9, Mount Shasta, CA 96067. U.S. $26/yr.
- *El Tratado de Libre Comercio: Entre el Viejo y el Nuevo Orden*, by Bárbara Driscoll de Alvarado and Mónica Gambrill C. 1992. 268 pages.
- *Implicaciones Jurídicas de la Apertura Comercial*, by J.J. de Olloquí. 1991. 142 pages.
- *La Administración Bush*, by Consuelo Paz Márquez and Mónica Verea Campos, editors. 1991. 210 pages.

Centro de Investigación para el Desarrollo (CIDAC)

Jaime Balmes 11, Edificio D
Col. Polanco
México, D.F. 11510
Phone: (5) 3-95-88-44
Fax: (5) 3-95-91-74
International Mail: c/o International Messengers, PO Box 60326, Houston, TX 77205.
Contact: Luis Rubio F.

DESCRIPTION

Government funded, CIDAC boasts a research staff trained in political science, economics, sociology, history, education, and human development.

ACTIVITIES

The center's projects focus on housing and governmental separation of powers.

RESOURCES

- A series of books on critical political and economic issues ranging from industrial policy to the Pacific Basin. The first four books in the series were published in 1988; the final two (one on the impact of the U.S.-Canada Free Trade Agreement upon Mexico; the other on technological policy) in 1992.

Colegio de la Frontera Norte (COLEF)*

Blvd. Abelardo L. Rodríguez 21
Zona del Río
Tijuana, B.C. 22320
Phone: (66) 30-04-11
Fax: (66) 30-00-50
U.S. mailing address: PO Box "L", Chula Vista, CA 92912
Contact: Dr. Jorge Carrillo V., Academic General Director

DESCRIPTION

Founded in 1982, the Colegio de la Frontera Norte is a decentralized, public, academic institution with a regional scope, focusing on the U.S.-Mexico borderlands. COLEF boasts 75 full-time researchers and offers three postgraduate degrees (M.A.'s) in regional development, applied economics, and population. The college's central objectives are: to develop recommendations for the optimum planning of the economic, social, and cultural development of the region; to identify and study sources of conflict between Mexico and the United States; and to train graduates in all facets of the northern border region.

ACTIVITES

COLEF coordinates more than twenty seminars annually, and participates in most forums dealing with the Mexico-U.S. region. A sampling of research project titles at its main campus, COLEF-Tijuana, include: The Free Trade Agreement and the Northern Borderlands; Borderland Agriculture; The Restructuring of the Manufacturing Industry in Northern Mexico; System of Environmental Preservation for the Mexico-U.S. Border; Transboundary Water Management of the two Nogales Areas; Decentralized System of Water Treatment (SIDETRAN); Perspectives on Modernization and Social Change; The Employment Market in the Maquiladoras; Labor's Restructuration in the Mexican Auto Industry; The Maquiladora Industry of Northern Mexico: 1982-1990 Industrial Restructuring; Transnationals and the Free Trade Agreement–A Case Study; Union's Strategies in the face of the Modernization of Labor–A Study of the Maquiladora and Mining Industries; Demographic Changes and Interrelationships in the Mexico-U.S. Border; Narcotraffic and Free Trade in the Mexico-U.S. Border, 1992-1993; Regulations and Impact of a Free Trade Agreement on Northern Mexico; Integration of (Alta) California with Mexico.

COLEF-Mexicali focuses on the future of Mexican agriculture under NAFTA, the urban use of water in Mexicali, environmentally acceptable management of transboundary water, and binational implications in the distribution of the waters of the Colorado River.

COLEF-Nogales concentrates on primary health care and environmental risks in the Nogales area.

COLEF-Juarez examines the impact of NAFTA on cultural industries, living standards in Juárez, *maquiladoras*, industrialization, the environment and urban development.

COLEF-Nuevo Laredo is the base for a project that studies the history of the Mexico-U.S. borderlands.

COLEF-Monterrey investigates productivity analysis of Mexican and U.S. industry, and social impacts of the *maquiladora* industry.

COLEF-Matamoros, in conjunction with COLEF-Monterrey, focuses on private-sector strategies toward free trade, the development and introduction of new technologies, the comparative productivity of industries on both sides of the border, labor unions in northern Mexico, and the role of women in the economy and development of the region.

LINKS

COLEF is a member of UC MEXUS, PROFMEX, ANUIES, and CONACYT. Some faculty are members of the Association of Borderlands Scholars.

RESOURCES

- *El Medio Ambiente como Fuente de Conflicto en la Relación Binacional México-Estados Unidos*, by Roberto Sánchez Rodríguez. 1990.
- *The International Guide to Research on Mexico*. A compilation of foreign research projects on Mexico published every two years in collaboration with the Center for U.S.-Mexican Studies of UCSD.
- *Boletín El Correo Fronterizo*. Bimonthly bulletin. U.S. $10/yr.
- *Colección COLEF*. A series of books authored by COLEF faculty.
- *Colección Cuadernos*. A monograph series.
- *Revista Frontera Norte*. Scientific research. Bilingual. U.S. $25/yr.
- *Journal Rio Bravo*. A binational, bilingual social sciences magazine published jointly by the University of Texas at Edinburg and COLEF-Monterrey.
- *The Impact of Free Trade on the Citrus Industry of Nuevo León*. A joint publication of COLEF-Monterrey and Nuevo León University.

OTHER OFFICES

Colegio de la Frontera Norte-Ciudad Juárez
Av. Campestre 100
Campestre Juárez
Ciudad Juárez, Chih. 32460
Phone: (16) 17-57-02 Fax: (16) 17-89-58
U.S. mailing address: PO Box 1385, El Paso, TX 79948
Contact: Eduardo Barrera

Colegio de la Frontera Norte-Matamoros
Av. Alvaro Obregón 12
Edif. Rebeca #315, Col. Jardín
Matamoros, Tamps.
Phone/fax: (891) 3-45-59
U.S. mailing address: PO Box 2136, Brownsville, TX 78522
Contact: Cirila Quintero Ramírez

Colegio de la Frontera Norte-Mexicali*
Calafia e Independencia 1096 #1
Centro Cívico
Mexicali, B.C. 21000
Phone: (65) 57-53-41 Fax: (65) 57-25-89
U.S. mailing address: PO Box 8220, Calexico, CA 92231
Contact: Jesús Adolfo Román Calleros, Regional Director of the Dirección Regional del Noroeste, or Francisco A. Bernal Rodríguez

Colegio de la Frontera Norte-Monterrey
Bolivia 313, Col. Vista Hermosa
Monterrey, N.L. 64620
Phone: (83) 48-57-03
Contact: Victor Zúñiga, Regional Director of the Dirección Regional de Noreste

Colegio de la Frontera Norte-Nogales
Calle Campodónico 303, Col. Granja
Nogales, Son. 84065
Phone: (631) 3-04-26 Fax: (631) 3-21-85
U.S. mailing address: PO Box 3048, Nogales, AZ 85628
Contact: Franciso Lara Valencia, Coordinator, or Irasema Coronado

Colegio de la Frontera Norte-Nuevo Laredo
Chihuahua 2509, Col. Guerrero
Nuevo Laredo, Tamps. 88240
Phone: (871) 5-12-63 Fax: (871) 5-82-63
U.S. mailing address: PO Box 6415, Laredo, TX 78042
Contact: Manuel Ceballos Ramírez, Coordinator

Colegio de la Frontera Norte-Piedras Negras
Progreso y Hacienda 503, Col. Burocratas
Piedras Negras, Coah. 26020
Phone: (878) 2-53-00 Fax: (878) 2-50-20
U.S. mailing address: PO Box 7235, Eagle Pass, TX 78853
Contact: Camilo Contreras Delgado or Francisco René Vidaurrázaga O.

Colegio de México (COLMEX)

Camino al Ajusco 20
Col. Pedregal Sta. Teresa
México, D.F. 10740
Phone: (5) 6-45-59-55

DESCRIPTION

As the most prestigious university in Mexico, COLMEX has a special influence, both in academic and in policy circles. Many alumni are now in senior government positions, affording COLMEX superior access to data and resources. Top names at COLMEX include Lorenzo Meyer (history and political science), Sergio Aguayo (security issues), and Carlos Rico (political economy). Experts at COLMEX are often quoted by the international media.

Colegio de México has seven centers; we have listed the two most relevant below.

Centro de Estudios Económicos*
Contact: Adalberto García Rocha, Director

The federal government provides 70 percent of the Centro de Estudios Económicos' funding. The center employs 16 professors who concentrate on three primary disciplines: Public Finance, Income Distribution, and International Economics.

Programa de Estudios sobre Estados Unidos y Canadá
Contact: Gustavo Vega (ext. 145)

Jointly with the Centre for Trade Policy and Law (Carleton University, Ottawa, Canada), Programa de Estudios operates a North American Economic Integration Project to determine the industrial sectors for which there is the greatest possibility to successfully negotiate trade agreements. The program has undertaken a survey of 1,500 firms in the three countries to determine their internationality and their reactions to the ideas of trade and sectoral agreements. It also conducts in-depth interviews with top business and political leaders in the countries, and makes policy recommendations.

RESOURCES

- *Estudios Económicos*. Biannual magazine with applied and quantitative economics as the primary focus.

Colegio de Sonora*

Av. Obregón 54
Col. Centro
Hermosillo, Son. 83000
Phone: (62) 12-50-21/65-51
Fax: (62) 12-00-15
Contact: Catalina A. Denman, Director

DESCRIPTION

Colegio de Sonora (Sonora College) researches the social problems of the region, disseminating its results in publications, conferences, and courses.

ACTIVITIES

Members of Sonora College have participated in: 1) the Binational Committee on Health of the two Nogales (Arizona and Sonora), which studies primary health care, occupational health, and the environment, as well as promoting the health and environment network of activists and academics in the border region; 2) a history of relations between Sonora and Arizona, 1940-1990; 3) a project analyzing the implications and possible effects of the English Only movement in Arizona on binational relations; 4) a forum on the cultural effects of NAFTA; 5) an analysis of border urbanization; and 6) organizing the Sonora Forum on the Free Trade Agreement.

RESOURCES

- *Gaceta de El Colegio de Sonora*. Quarterly bulletin.
- *Revista de El Colegio de Sonora*. Annual.
- *Revista Estudios Sociales*. Quarterly magazine.
- "Los Mexiconorteamericanos Arizonenses y los Sonorenses," by Leopoldo Santos Ramírez and Rosario Navarro Nogales in *Gaceta de El Colegio de Sonora*. Working Paper #5, April-June 1991.
- *Las repercusiones de la industria maquiladora de exportación en la salud: el peso al nacer de hijos de obreras en Nogales*, by Catalina Denman. Working Paper #2. El Colegio de Sonora, 1991.
- *Las relaciones de Sonora con Arizona*, by Leopoldo Santos Ramírez.
- *El narcotráfico en las relaciones México-Estados Unidos*, by Leopoldo Santos Ramírez.

Escuela Nacional de Estudios Profesionales — Acatlán (ENEP)*

Universidad Nacional Autónoma de México (UNAM)
Av. Alcanfores y San Juan Totoltepec s/n
Col. Sta. Cruz Acatlán
Naucalpan, Edo. de Méx. 53150
Phone: (5) 3-73-88-78/22-92 ext. 167
Fax: (5) 5-60-75-54
Contact: Arturo Sabino Arcos Avila

DESCRIPTION

ENEP's Master's program in U.S.-Mexican Studies seeks to analyze the economic, political, social, historical, and cultural aspects of bilateral relationships.

ACTIVITIES

The program sponsors academic encounters between Mexican students in ENEP, and students and professors at the Latin American Institute of the University of New Mexico.

RESOURCES

- *Revista Posgrado de Acatlán*. Quarterly. $30,000 M.N.

Grupo de Economistas y Asociados (GEA)

Pestalozzi 522
Col. del Valle
México, D.F. 03020
Phone: (5) 5-36-19-22
Fax: (5) 5-23-41-42
Contact: Jesús Reyes Heroles

DESCRIPTION

GEA is a private organization of 30 partners specialized in economics, political science, finance, and statistics that conducts consulting and research activities. Its purpose is to provide information and analysis to government, business, and other private organizations in Mexico and abroad.

ACTIVITIES

GEA analyzes domestic and international economies in order to advise producer associations preparing themselves for negotiations related to the free trade agreement. It is also a source of information about the political and labor climates in Mexico.

RESOURCES

- *Economic Report*. Monthly report on the Mexican economy. Free to GEA clients.
- *Political Report*. Semimonthly report with political events and electoral agendas.
- A data bank on Mexican unions, including information on their composition, organizational structure, leadership, statutes, and prospects.
- A monthly report on labor conflicts and negotiations in Mexico.

Instituto de Estudios de Estados Unidos (IEEU)*

Centro de Investigación y Docencia Económica (CIDE)
Carretera México-Toluca Km 16.5
Col. Lomas de Sta. Fe
México, D.F. 01210
Phone: (5) 2-59-12-10 ext. 311
Fax: (5) 5-70-42-77
Contact: Guadalupe González, Director

DESCRIPTION

The institute has four areas of study: 1) Mexico-U.S. relations, focusing on mutual perceptions and interactions, and discussion of Mexico in the U.S. Congress; 2) U.S. domestic politics, especially territorial expansion, and the neoconservative movement in the United States; 3) the U.S. economy; and 4) U.S. foreign policy, notably the U.S. policy of democracy promotion for Latin America.

LINKS

The IEEU is a member of PROFMEX.

RESOURCES

- *Estados Unidos: Informe Trimestral*. U.S. $34/yr.

Seminario Permanente de Estudios Chicanos y de Fronteras*

Dirección de Etnología y Antropología Social (DEAS)
Instituto Nacional de Antropología e Historia (INAH)
Plaza del Carmen 4 y 6
Col. San Angel
México, D.F. 01000
Phone: (5) 5-50-80-43/05-32
Fax: (5) 6-59-48-37
Contact: Dr. Juan Manuel Sandoval, General Coordinator

DESCRIPTION

Seminario Permanente de Estudios Chicanos y de Fronteras (Permanent Seminar on Chicano and Border Studies) is a research and academic program of DEAS-INAH. The program links students of borderland issues with various social, political, cultural, academic, and labor organizations in order to assess issues of labor struggles on both sides of the border. Some topics of investigation include the function of Mexican consulates in the United States in relation to the rights of undocumented workers, the Mexican northern border and U.S. national security, the influence of the treaties defining territorial boundaries, the meaning of economic and political dependency, the impact of the Simpson-Rodino Law, Mixteca immigration, and Latino immigrant attitudes toward unions. The Permanent Seminar also coordinates Sin Fronteras (Without Borders) International Cultural Center—a network of various groups from the United States, Mexico, Central America, and the Caribbean.

ACTIVITIES

A sampling of the forums and conferences it has helped to organize include: U.S.-Mexico Conference on International Capital Mobility and Binational Labor Organizing; Chicanos, Pachucos, and Cholos; Mixteca Immigration; Perspectives of Chicano Politics; and Maquiladoras in Mexico.

LINKS

The Seminario Permanente collaborates with the International Center for Chicano, Border, and Immigrant Labor Studies (Los Angeles, CA), the Community Studies Workshop (Chicago, IL), the National Network for Immigrant and Refugee Rights, the National Association for Chicano Studies, the RMALC, and the Border Commission for Human Rights.

RESOURCES

- *Frontera Norte, Chicanos, Pachucos y Cholos*, by Luis Hernández Palacios and Juan Manuel Sandoval, editors. Universidad Autónoma Zacatecas and UAM. 1989.
- *Maquiladoras: Migración y Fuerza de Trabajo Femenina*, by Arcelia Tánori. Colección de Divulgación del INAH, 1989.
- *Internacionalización de la Fuerza de Trabajo y Acumulación de Capital: México-Estados Unidos*, by Jesús Antonio Machuca. Colección Científica del INAH, 1990.
- *El Tratado de Libre Comercio México-Estados Unidos*. Manual for the Discussion and Analysis Workshops of the Permanent Seminar on Chicano and Border Studies. Documents for Discussion #1. March 1991.
- *Las Fronteras Nacionales en el Umbral de dos Siglos*, by Juan Manuel Sandoval, editor. INAH.
- Center for Documentation and Information: bibliographic and newspaper archives, and an audio-visual loaning section.

Universidad Autónoma Metropolitana — Azcapotzalco (UAM-A)

Av. San Pablo 180
Col. Reynosa Tamaulipas
México, D.F. 02200
Phone: (5) 5-57-67-08
Fax: (5) 3-95-39-02
Contact: Silvia Ortega Salazar, Rector of the UAM-A

DESCRIPTION

The UAM is a public university similar to the UNAM in that the humanities play an important role in the general orientation of the university, but UAM differs from UNAM in two ways: its decentralized administrative structure (UAM has three campuses in Mexico City: Azcapotzalco, Iztapalapa, and Xochimilco, each with its own dean), and its academic structure, based on a system of modular studies. UAM promotes academic links with U.S. universities.

LINKS

UAM-A serves as the seat for the Secretary General of PROFMEX.

RESOURCES

- *El Cotidiano*. Bimonthly magazine analyzing the current state of political affairs. $42,000 M.N./yr. in Mexico City, U.S. $30/yr. in other countries. Of special interest is issue #43, September-October 1991, entitled *Tratado de Libre Comercio: Trabajo y Ecología*.
- *Trabajo*. Magazine about society, technology, and cultural issues funded by the Friedrich Ebert Foundation. Biannual, $10,000 M.N. Of special interest is #5-6, Winter-Spring 1991, entitled "Debate: Tratado de Libre Comercio: AFL-CIO, COECE, CANACINTRA, CNTE, CTM, FAT, SME, SNTE . . ." $10,000 M.N.
- *Boletín de Análisis Económico*. Of special interest is #2, 1991 entitled "Tratado de Libre Comercio: Mexico, Canada, Estados Unidos."
- Books and other publications in conjunction with PROFMEX. Magazines and other publications of UAM-A can be obtained from: División de Ciencias Sociales y Humanidades, Edificio E, Cubículo 004, A.P. 32-031, México, D.F. 06031. Phone: 3-82-50-00, ext. 151.

3. UNITED STATES

Association of Borderlands Scholars*

University of Texas at El Paso, Dept. of Political Science
El Paso, TX 79968
Phone: (915) 747-5227
Fax: (915) 747-5111
Contact: Richard Bath

DESCRIPTION

Convening scholars from a variety of disciplines and countries, the Association of Borderlands Scholars' focus is on the U.S.-Mexico border.

ACTIVITIES

The group sponsors international academic conferences, usually held along the U.S.-Mexico border.

RESOURCES

- *Journal of Borderlands Studies.*

Bildner Center for Western Hemisphere Studies

City University of New York (CUNY)
Graduate Center
33 W. 42nd St.
New York, NY 10036
Phone: (212) 642-2950
Fax: (212) 642-2789
Contact: Ronald G. Hellman, Director

DESCRIPTION

The Bildner Center sponsors research, seminars, and forums that address the practical resolution of public-policy problems facing nations of the Western Hemisphere. Part of the Graduate School of the City University of New York, it serves as a link between CUNY's intellectual community and other experts and policymakers working on contemporary issues in Latin America, North America, and the Caribbean.

ACTIVITIES

In 1991 the center hosted a seminar series to address current Mexican issues as part of its role as the PROFMEX Office of Policy Studies. Its November 1991 Fourth Annual Conference on U.S.-Mexico Relations addressed the subject: Mexico in a New Hemispheric Order.

LINKS

Member of PROFMEX.

Border Research Institute*

New Mexico State University
4200 Research Dr.
Las Cruces, NM 88003
Phone: (505) 646-3524
Fax: (505) 646-5474
Contact: Maria Telles-McGeagh, Director

DESCRIPTION

The institute is an information clearinghouse for government policy makers and the general public. It promotes cooperation between agricultural, business, and academic sectors in order to enhance opportunities for international trade and cultural exchange as well as awareness regarding the impact of NAFTA on the socioeconomic infrastructure of the border region.

LINKS

Affiliated with the Border Trade Alliance and the National Maquiladora Association.

RESOURCES

- *Border Bulletin.*
- *Borderlands Monograph Series.*
- *Latin American Research Monograph Series.*

Center for Immigration Studies (CIS)*

1815 H St. NW #1010
Washington, DC 20006-3604
Phone: (202) 466-8185/328-7228
Fax: (202) 466-8076
Contact: John Gwynn

DESCRIPTION

This nonprofit research and policy institute is devoted to the analysis of immigration's effect on the broad national interests of the United States—economic, social, demographic, and environmental.

RESOURCES

- *CIS Papers*. Specialized monographs addressing such issues as: illegal immigrants and job displacement of American workers, and immigration pressures from Mexico and the Caribbean.
- *CIS Backgrounders* and *Announcements*. Shorter assessments of current immigration developments. Of special interest is *CIS Backgrounder* No. 4, December 1991, entitled: *Immigration and Free Trade with Mexico: Protecting American Workers against Double Jeopardy*, by David Simcox, Director of the Center for Immigration Studies.

Center for Inter-American and Border Studies (CIABS)*

University of Texas at El Paso (UTEP)
Administration Bldg. #320
El Paso, TX 79968
Phone: (915) 747-5196
Fax: (915) 747-5574
Contact: Dr. Samuel Schmidt

DESCRIPTION

Involved in seminars, consortiums, exhibits, lectures, and research, CIABS also serves as the center for transborder faculty contacts among PROFMEX membership in the three countries.

ACTIVITIES

Activities include the study of local and regional issues such as free trade and the environment; disseminating information on Mexico in the United States and vice versa; publishing scholarly articles on border issues; and expanding the center's role to include studying Mexico as a whole as well as U.S. policy relating to that country.

LINKS

Member of PROFMEX.

RESOURCES

- *Border Issues*. $5 each issue.
- *PROFMEX Special Papers*. Distributed as part of its role as PROFMEX's Office of Special Papers and Mexican Exchange.

Center for International Policy*

1755 Massachusetts Ave. NW #324
Washington, DC 20036
Phone: (202) 232-3317
Fax: (202) 232-3440
Contact: Rosemary Gutierrez

DESCRIPTION

This nonprofit education and research organization analyzes issues concerning U.S. policy toward the third world and its impact on human rights and human needs.

ACTIVITIES

The center's Mexico Project analyzes the social effects of the proposed economic integration of Mexico with the rest of North America. It advocates inclusion in NAFTA of guarantees of labor rights, environmental protection, and the subsidizing of adjustment costs for those most adversely affected by the changes.

LINKS

Member of MODTLE.

Center for Strategic and International Studies (CSIS)

1800 K St. NW #400
Washington, DC 20006
Phone: (202) 775-3180
Fax: (202) 775-3199
Contact: M. Delal Baer (Mexico) or Sidney Weintraub (Canada)

DESCRIPTION

The CSIS, a conservative think tank founded in 1962, maintains close links to the U.S. policymaking establishment. The CSIS concentrates on national-security issues and on promoting U.S. economic interests. Current and former top-level government officials serve as CSIS fellows, attend its study groups, or sit on its advisory board. The organization's Americas Program, established in 1990, has multiple components and is designed to focus research and policy attention on changes in the Western Hemisphere. Canadian Studies and Mexican Studies are two central components of the Americas Program; both focus on North American free trade issues but also include other areas of study, such as politics, economics, immigration, and narcotics.

ACTIVITIES

Through the Canadian and Mexican Studies programs, the CSIS sponsors conferences, seminars, and research programs. These programs include participants from the political, corporate, media, and academic communities in the United States, Canada, and Mexico. The CSIS also co-sponsors conferences, forums, and research programs with counterpart organizations and universities in Mexico and Canada. For instance, a 1991 conference on free trade was co-hosted with Canada's Fraser Institute (Vancouver), the Centre for International Studies (University of Toronto), and Stanford University's Americas Program. The CSIS's Mexico Studies project includes a Congressional Study Group on Mexico, chaired by members of the U.S. Senate and House of Representatives. The study group meets quarterly to discuss issues such as trade, economic conditions and policies, immigration, drug traffic, and foreign policy. The objectives include developing bipartisan policy statements and recommendations, and increasing linkages between the U.S. and Mexican congresses.

RESOURCES

- *Investing in Security: Economic Aid for Non-Economic Purposes*, by Penelope Hartland-Thunberg. Includes case study on Mexico. Forthcoming 1992.
- *Strategic Sectors in Mexican-U.S. Free Trade*, edited by M. Delal Baer and Guy F. Erb. 1991. $9.95.
- *The Congress and Mexico: Bordering on Change*, by Senators Pete Wilson and Lloyd Bentsen. Report of the CSIS Congressional Study Group on Mexico. 1989. $6.95
- *Canada's Identity Crisis: A Background Review*, by Ben Tonra.
- *From the Yukon to the Yucatán: Creating a New Vision for Trade in North America*, by Representative Jim Kolbe.
- *Ten Considerations Favoring Free Trade with Mexico*, by Sidney Weintraub.
- *Beyond Coexistence: The United States and Mexico*, by Alan Stoga.
- *The North American Free Trade Agreement: Some Environmental Considerations*, by Jan Gilbreath Rich.
- *Free Trade and the Environment: Background to the Debate and Implications for NAFTA*, by Udi Helman and Ben Tonra.
- *Canada in a Dynamic Global Economy*, by William A. McDonald.

Center for U.S.-Mexican Studies*

University of California at San Diego
La Jolla, CA 92093-0510
Phone: (619) 534-4503
Fax: (619) 534-6447
Contact: Coleen Lassegard, Assistant Director of Studies and Programs

DESCRIPTION

This program is the nation's largest devoted exclusively to the study of Mexico and U.S.-Mexican relations. It encompasses research in all of the social sciences and history, graduate and undergraduate student training, continuing professional education, publication of scholarly works, and public education activities that address the full range of problems affecting economic and political relations between Mexico and the United States. The center also studies the history, economy, political system, and social structure of Mexico; aspects of the U.S. economy and U.S. public policy that affect Mexico; and Mexico's economic interactions with Japan and other Pacific Basin countries.

ACTIVITIES

Through its Visiting Research Fellowship Program, the center annually sponsors the research of 20 to 25 predoctoral and postdoctoral scholars, journalists, and other nonacademic specialists, who spend from three to nine months in residence. Typically, people from Mexico receive over half of these fellowships, awarded through an open international competition. Each summer, in collaboration with UCSD's American Political Institutions Program, the center conducts a six-week Seminar in Studies of the United States, for 20 Latin American social scientists and nonacademic professionals. The center's research library and its interdisciplinary weekly Seminar on Mexico and U.S.-Mexico Relations, attract leading researchers from throughout the United States, Mexico, and other countries.

The center has a very active public education program, including frequent briefings for journalists, business executives, public officials, and community groups. Major research areas include: 1) North American economic integration in light of comparative studies of how free trade arrangements have worked in various regions of the world; 2) Mexico's economic relations with Japan, including a look at ties between Japanese firms operating in Mexico and the United States, and comparative studies of Japanese investment in other Latin American countries; 3) Mexican migration to the United States, with a focus on the problems and needs of immigrant children in California public schools, the impacts of Mexican immigration on San Diego County, the role of immigrant-owned businesses in promoting social mobility, and the problems in controlling illegal immigration; 4) the interaction of local and national interests in U.S.-Mexican relations, including the emergence of cross-border coalitions of grassroots organizations; 5) environmental problems both in Mexico and in U.S.-Mexico borderlands, with special attention to water-supply issues, transborder sewage flows, the environmental impacts of a North American free trade zone, and the management of Mexico City's environmental crisis; 6) social and political consequences of economic restructuring in Mexico, especially related to employment and income distribution; 7) multi-year research projects exploring the changing role of domestic interest groups in U.S.-Mexican relations; the impact of immigration on the San Diego/Tijuana area; intellectual property and direct-foreign-investment issues; the trilateral economic relationship between the United States, Japan, and Latin America; and the potential ramifications of the Enterprise for the Americas Initiative (EAI).

RESOURCES

The center produces hundreds of publications relating to U.S.-Mexican relations. Only a few examples are listed here.

- *Manufacturing Across Borders and Oceans: Japan, The United States, and Mexico*, edited by Gabriel Székely. 1991. $20.
- *The Changing Role of Mexican Labor in the U.S. Economy, Sectoral Perspectives*, edited by Wayne A. Cornelius. 1991. $25.
- *Maquiladoras, Annotated Bibliography and Research Guide to Mexico's In-Bond Industry, 1980-1988*, by Leslie Sklair. 1989. 215 pages. $18.
- The series *Dimensions of U.S.-Mexican Relations*, edited by Rosario Green and Peter H. Smith, 1989, is based on papers prepared for the Bilateral Commission on the Future of United States-Mexican Relations. Five volumes: 1) *Images of Mexico in The United States*, edited by John H. Coatsworth and Carlos Rico; 2) *The Economics of Interdependence*, edited by William Glade and Cassio Luiselli; 3) *Mexican Migration to the United States: Origins, Consequences, and Policy Options*, edited by Wayne A Cornelius and Jorge A. Bustamante; 4) *The Drug Connection in U.S.-Mexican Relations*, edited by Marta Tienda and Guadalupe González; 5) *Foreign Policy in U.S.-Mexican Relations*, edited by Rosario Green and Peter H. Smith. $12 to $16 each volume. The complete five-volume series is also available for $60.
- *Guía Internacional de Investigaciones sobre México / International Guide to Research on Mexico*, published biennially jointly by the Center for U.S.-Mexican Studies, Colegio de la Frontera Norte, and Colegio de México. Projects are indexed by subject, researcher, and institution where the research is being conducted. 1989-1990 Edition. $15 for individuals, $25 for institutions.

Council on Foreign Relations*

58 E. 68th St.
New York, NY 10021
Phone: (212) 734-0400
Fax: (212) 861-1916
Contact: Heidi Gifford, NAFTA project

DESCRIPTION

The council, established in 1921, recruits membership by invitation only. Members include a bipartisan range of influential U.S. citizens with expertise in international relations and foreign policy issues.

ACTIVITIES

The council hosts meetings, conferences, and study sessions about topics of current importance in international affairs with attendance by invitation only. It is conducting one grant-funded project on NAFTA, involving 78 current policymakers and invited guests in approximately ten meetings over an 18-month period.

RESOURCES

- *Foreign Affairs*. Quarterly. $38/yr.
- A series of monographs on the findings of the NAFTA study group should be available by December 1992.

Economic Policy Institute (EPI)*

1730 Rhode Island Ave. NW #200
Washington, DC 20036
Phone: (202) 775-8810
Fax: (202) 775-0819
Contact: Thea Lee

DESCRIPTION

This progressive, policy-oriented research group sponsors conferences, conducts seminars, and publishes reports and briefing papers on economic issues. Its goal is to identify a new economic strategy that can provide prosperous, fair, and balanced growth as America moves toward the 21st century.

RESOURCES

- *Fast Track-Fast Shuffle: The Economic Consequences of the Administration's Proposed Trade Agreement with Mexico*, by Jeff Faux, President, EPI and Richard Rothstein. Briefing paper. $5.
- *U.S. Jobs and the Mexico Trade Proposal*, by J. Faux and W. Spriggs. May 1991. $5.

Heritage Foundation*

214 Massachusetts Ave. NE
Washington, DC 20002-4999
Phone: (202) 546-4400
Fax: (202) 544-2260
Contact: Michael G. Wilson or Wesley Smith

DESCRIPTION

This conservative research institute, founded in 1973, promotes public policies aimed at reducing government regulation of business, shrinking government expenditures for social programs, stimulating free enterprise, and strengthening the U.S. military. It is a strong promoter both of NAFTA and of President Bush's Enterprise for the Americas Initiative (EAI).

ACTIVITIES

The foundation develops and promotes policy recommendations through research, publications, lectures, debates, seminars, briefings, and conferences. It also provides witnesses to testify at congressional committee hearings. The Heritage Foundation has urged a U.S.-Mexico free trade accord since 1981, and established a multifaceted "Mexico Project" because of Mexico's singular importance to the United States. Since 1981, its main focus has been a free trade accord, with tangential interest in the environment and human rights.

A special "Mexico Working Group" includes personnel from the U.S. executive branch, the business community, the Mexican government, the media, and academia, as well as congressional representatives and staffers. At working group meetings, U.S. and Mexican policymakers or other influential conservative experts discuss aspects of U.S.-Mexico relations, especially the proposed NAFTA, its potential effects, and other trade and investment topics. The purpose of the working group is to generate policy proposals and to act as a forum for educating participants and questioning policymakers. The foundation sponsored a pro-NAFTA conference in November 1991, and a new project supports the EAI. A visiting-fellowship program attracts Mexican researchers to the Heritage Foundation for short-term research and analysis.

RESOURCES

- *Heritage Foundation Backgrounder, Heritage Lecture, Backgrounder Update*, and *Issue Bulletin*. Each issue of these publications is devoted to a single aspect of U.S.-Mexico or U.S.-Canada-Mexico relations. $3 per issue.
- *Mexico Watch*. Monthly. $1.50 per issue.
- "The U.S. and Mexico: Setting a New Agenda," *Heritage Lecture* #210. 1989. 234 pages. $12.50.
- "Refuting Six Myths about the U.S.-Mexico Free Trade Accord," *Backgrounder* #818, March 1991.
- "Why Bush Needs the 'Fast Track' for Trade Negotiations," *Issue Bulletin*, April 1991.
- "The United States-Mexico Free Trade Agreement: Prospects for Hispanics," *Heritage Lecture* #315, by Representative Bill Richardson. 1991.
- "Guidelines for U.S. Negotiators at the Trade Talks with Mexico," *Backgrounder* #861, October 18, 1991.
- "Political Reform in Mexico: Salinas's Other Revolution," *Backgrounder* #858, October 1991.
- "U.S.-Canada-Mexico: A Free Trade Partnership for the 21st Century," proceedings of the November 13-14 conference on NAFTA.
- "Improving America's Global Competitiveness Under a North American Free Trade Agreement," *Heritage Lecture* #359, by Senator John McCain, November 14, 1991.
- "How the North American Free Trade Agreement Creates Jobs," *Backgrounder* #872, January 15, 1992.
- "Privatization in Mexico: Much Better, But Still Not Enough," *Backgrounder Update* #172, January 20, 1992.
- "The NAFTA and the Enterprise for the Americas Initiative: A Blueprint for Economic Expansion from Alaska to Antarctica," *Heritage Lecture* #375, by David C. Mulford, March 4, 1992.
- "Protecting the Environment in North America with Free Trade," *Backgrounder* #889, April 2, 1992.

Institute for Regional Studies of the Californias (IRSC)*

San Diego State University
San Diego, CA 92182-0435
Phone: (619) 594-5423
Fax: (619) 594-5474
Contact: Paul Ganster

ACTIVITIES

Environment, Development, and the Common Good promotes public outreach and education on environmental issues in a binational border context.

Public Policy and Border Environmental Issues hosts workshops with researchers, government officials, and environmentalists to develop specific approaches to and solutions for border environmental problems.

LINKS

Member of PROFMEX.

RESOURCES

- *Mexico Policy News*. Newsletter published several times per year for PROFMEX. $30/yr. for individual membership.
- *The Unionization of the Maquiladora Industry: The Tamaulipan Case National Context*, by Edward J. Williams and John T. Passé-Smith. 1992. 134 pages. $12.50.

Institute of the Americas*

10111 N. Torrey Pines Rd.
La Jolla, CA 92037
Phone: (619) 453-5560
Fax: (619) 435-2165
Contact: Lee Tablewski

DESCRIPTION

This independent, nonprofit institution is devoted to finding effective responses to some of the major challenges facing the countries of the Western Hemisphere: consolidating democracy and market-oriented economic reforms; extending free trade; countering drug abuse and traffic; and halting environmental deterioration. The institute's contributions to these tasks during its first decade have earned it a reputation as a pragmatic think tank working at the forefront of change in the Americas.

ACTIVITIES

Free Trade in the Americas is a long-term project that sponsors high-level consultations on a realistic strategy for extending free trade to the entire hemisphere.

RESOURCES

- *HEMISFILE*. Bimonthly publication of political and economic trends in the Americas. The November 1991 issue assesses prospects and problems for hemispheric free trade. $38/yr. for North America; $45/yr. all other countries.

Interamerican Dialogue*

11 Dupont Circle NW #502
Washington, DC 20036-1207
Phone: (202) 265-5350
Fax: (202) 265-5425
Contact: Richard Feinberg, President

DESCRIPTION

The group produces research and policy recommendations on U.S.-Latin American relations, hemispheric trade issues, democratic governance, poverty, education, narcotics, etc. Projects are designed to influence the policy community and to focus attention on Latin America.

ACTIVITIES

A popular education and research project examines hemispheric integration, beyond just the United States, Mexico, and Canada.

Inter-Hemispheric Education Resource Center*

PO Box 4506
Albuquerque, NM 87196-4506
Phone: (505) 842-8288
Fax: (505) 246-1601
Email: (PeaceNet) resourcectr
Contact: Debra Preusch

DESCRIPTION

This private, nonprofit research and policy institute produces books, policy reports, and audiovisuals about Mexico, Central America, and the Caribbean concerning such issues as U.S. foreign aid, low-intensity conflict, land and hunger, and the role of private U.S. organizations and churches.

ACTIVITIES

Co-sponsored by the Mexican group Equipo Pueblo and the Action Canada Network, the Cross-Border Links Project is a clearinghouse and networking center for groups with a working interest in the changing relations between the United States, Canada, and Mexico. The goals of this project are to increase access to information about trilateral relations and to bolster existing networking efforts.

RESOURCES

- *Mexico: A Country Guide*, by Tom Barry. Covers Mexican society, politics, and economy in the 1990s. Fully referenced; includes photos, tables, charts, and index. January 1992. 401 pages. $11.95 plus $2.50 postage for U.S. orders.
- *Cross-Border Links*. An annotated listing of fair-trade networks, labor, environmental, and social-justice groups, academic and think-tank institutions, government agencies, and business groups that focus on relations among Mexico, Canada, and the United States. Edited jointly with Equipo Pueblo and Action Canada Network. August 1992. $11.95 plus $2.50 postage for U.S. orders.
- *Mexico InfoPak: A Briefing Book for Community Leaders*. A packet produced jointly with the Southwest Voter Research Institute. Thirteen pull-out sections with key facts related to Mexico's political system, economy, environment, and human rights situation, as well as to the issues involved in negotiating NAFTA. February 1992. $5 postpaid. Bulk discounts available.
- *Resource Center Bulletin*. Quarterly. Of special interest are *Bulletin* #23, Spring 1991, *Mexico Opens Up—United States Moves In*, which looks at the effect of NAFTA on the Mexican economy, and at the food and land crisis in Mexico; and *Bulletin* #27, Spring 1992, *Rethinking the Economics of Free Trade*. $5/yr. U.S. subscriptions, $10/yr. foreign subscriptions.
- *Extraños No Más*. Pocket-size booklet in Spanish with information about deportation, amnesty, temporary work permits, legal rights, and living in the United States. November 1991. 48 pages, $2 postpaid. Bulk discounts available.
- *BorderLines*. Quarterly publication monitoring organizing efforts along the U.S.-Mexico border. $10/yr.

International Transboundary Resource Center (CIRT)*

University of New Mexico Law School
1117 Stanford NE
Albuquerque, NM 87131
Phone: (505) 277-4820
Contact: Albert E. Utton, Director

DESCRIPTION

CIRT strives to improve policymaking related to the rational and equitable use of transboundary resources with full respect for the territorial sovereignty of each state concerned.

RESOURCES

- *Natural Resources Journal.* Policy-oriented quarterly (published by UNM's School of Law) dedicated to contributing to the improvement of public policy relating to the management and allocation of precious natural resources. Previous publications of the journal examine *U.S.-Mexico Transboundary Resource Issues*, and *U.S.-Canada Transboundary Resource Issues*.
- *Transboundary Resources Report.* Quarterly.

Latin America Data Base (LADB)*

Latin American Institute
University of New Mexico
801 Yale NE
Albuquerque, NM 87131-1016
Phone: (505) 277-6839
Fax: (505) 277-5989
Email: (PeaceNet) ladb
Contact: Roma Arellano

DESCRIPTION

LADB digests news stories from international wire services, shortwave radio broadcasts, and Mexican newspapers to produce electronic publishing containing current socioeconomic and political news on Latin America. By preempting and summarizing news before it appears in print, this group differs from clipping services and many other news sources on the region. Rather than merely translating or reprinting stories, LADB's researchers check the accuracy of sources in order to produce original articles. For topics that require in-depth examination, LADB affords extensive treatment, tapping sources and reports on developments and topics often ignored by the mainstream media.

RESOURCES

- *SourceMex: Economic News and Analysis on Mexico.* A compendium of news about private investment, trade, debt, inflation, public policy, *maquiladoras*, petroleum, agriculture, pollution, social welfare, etc. Published the first and third Wednesdays of each month. Analysis by Mexican journalists and scholars, published in both English and Spanish. $175/yr. for institutions, $115/yr. for individuals. For on-line access, LADB users have the option of subscribing to LADB at the University of New Mexico via direct or linked networks.

Latin American Institute (LAI)*

University of New Mexico
801 Yale NE
Albuquerque, NM 87131-1016
Phone: (505) 277-2961
Fax: (505) 277-5989
Contact: Dr. María Casellas-Kelly

DESCRIPTION

LAI promotes awareness of Latin America among the people of the state of New Mexico; develops outreach programs for public and private schools (K-12) on Latin America, as well as Spanish classes for the community; and collaborates with all levels of government as well as private organizations in the promotion of better understanding and relations between the United States and Latin America. The institute offers interdisciplinary degree programs on Latin America at B.A., M.A., and Ph.D. levels.

ACTIVITIES

LAI engages in academic collaboration and student exchanges with many universities and institutions in Mexico.

RESOURCES

- *Encounters-Latin American Research Review*. By subscription.
- *Research Papers*. Upon request.

Mexican Studies Program*

Center for Latin American Studies
University of Chicago
5848 S. University Ave.
Chicago, IL 60637
Phone: (312) 702-8963
Fax: (312) 702-1755
Contact: Friedrich Katz, Director; Michael Rosenfeld, Administrator; or Douglas Massey, Director of Latin American Studies.

DESCRIPTION

Inaugurated in 1991 by President Salinas, the program sponsors forums and seminars on Mexico.

ACTIVITIES

The Mexico Policy Forum convenes prominent Mexicans and Mexicanists to address audiences at the University of Chicago, the Chicago Council on Foreign Relations, and other institutions throughout the Midwest.

Mexico Policy Seminars. On a quarterly basis, the Mexican Studies Program brings leading scholars to the university to consider new perspectives on Mexican immigration.

Travel/Research Grants are awarded to faculty and graduate students who wish to undertake brief research projects on policy issues concerning Mexico or U.S.-Mexican relations.

RESOURCES

- *Mexico News Update*. Biweekly newsletter of English language translations of news from the Mexican press. Distributed upon request to anyone associated with the university.

NAFTA Project*

Dept. of Political Science
University of Oregon
Eugene, OR 97403-1284
Phone: (503) 346-4861
Fax: (503) 346-3660
Contact: Daniel Goldrich

DESCRIPTION

The NAFTA project concentrates on teaching, research, and community education (speakers, forums, panels, field trips to the U.S.-Mexico border) about the environmental, political, social, economic, and cultural impacts of NAFTA, in the context of global and regional economic integration. It engages in ongoing community (university and extra-university) education and awareness regarding NAFTA's environmental and social impacts, and maintains an interest in long-term intercommunity relations for this purpose.

LINKS

The NAFTA project interacts with the Labor Education and Research Center, as well as the Environmental Studies, and Latin American Studies departments at the University of Oregon.

North American Project*

The Americas Program
Stanford University
Encina Hall #200
Stanford, CA 94305-6055
Phone: (415) 725-0933
Fax: (415) 725-2592
Contact: Clark W. Reynolds, Director

DESCRIPTION

An outgrowth of the Project on U.S.-Mexico Relations founded in 1980, the North American Project brings together Canadian, Mexican, and U.S. scholars and decision-makers from the private and public sectors in workshops, seminars, and conferences whose aim is to stimulate and share research on changing economic and social relations among the three countries of North America. All activities of the North American Project are conceptualized, coordinated, researched, and funded on a trinational basis.

ACTIVITIES

The North American Project launched its conference in Toronto on The Dynamics of North American Trade and Economic Relations just one week before the June 1988 summit of OECD leaders in the same city. It also sponsored two workshops in Washington on Debt and Growth: The U.S. and Mexico in the Medium Term. Research areas include the debt crisis, structural adjustment, and economic growth.

RESOURCES

- "Essays on Comparative Advantage in North America: Theory and Policy," in *The North American Review of Economics and Finance* (1990/1991).
- "Case Studies of Dynamic Comparative Advantage in North America," in *The North American Review of Economics and Finance* (1990/1991).
- *The Dynamics of North American Trade and Investment: Canada, Mexico, and the United States*. Based on papers delivered at the Toronto conference. January 1991. The volume represents the first of several books with a focus on North American relations in the continuing *Series on U.S.-Mexico Relations*, published by Stanford University Press.
- *The Promotion of Micro and Small Enterprise Development in Mexico: A Preliminary Report*, by Clark W. Reynolds and Ana Paula Pessoa, produced for the Inter-American Development Bank. October 1991.
- *A United States Vision of Closer North American Economic Relations*, by Clark W. Reynolds, as written testimony for Senate Foreign Relations Committee Hearings: U.S.-Mexico Free Trade Agreement, March 22, 1991, and based upon author's chapter "A United States Vision of Closer North American Economics Relations," in *Continental Accord: North American Economic Integration*, edited by Steve Globerman, Fraser Institute. Vancouver, 1991.
- "North American Interdependence: Mexico's New Paradigm for the Nineties," by Clark W. Reynolds, produced for the School of Advanced International Studies and found in *Mexico's External Relations in the 1990's*. May 1990.
- Book being prepared on long-term approaches to Mexican debt and growth.

PROFMEX — The Consortium for Research on Mexico*

Executive Secretariat
1440 Euclid Ave.
Berkeley, CA 94708
Phone: (510) 486-1247
Fax: (510) 486-0338
Contact: George Baker, Executive Secretary

DESCRIPTION

This trinational, nonprofit organization boasts numerous branch offices and several purposes. It: 1) links individuals and institutions interested in contemporary Mexico and North American policy issues; 2) sponsors research; 3) hosts meetings; 4) maintains Secretariats in Mexico and the USA, and a Visitor's Center in Mexico City; 5) arranges trinational faculty/researcher exchanges; 6) advises on public policy; 7) coordinates an electronic information-exchange network; and 8) develops joint programs with ANUIES—Asociación Nacional de Universidades e Institutos de Enseñanza Superior. PROFMEX comprises 250 individual members and over 50 member organizations.

ACTIVITIES

PROFMEX activities include policy studies, academic research, trinational conferences, publications, and a cross-border policy project, focusing on housing and urban services in Ciudad Juárez-El Paso. It also organizes workshops and conferences on issues related to the U.S.-Mexico free trade agreement and its impact on the border region. Its MexNet electronic network offers on-line communication as well as email and bulletin board service, ranging from current and time-series basic economic data to international agricultural prices. In conjunction with ANUIES, PROFMEX organizes an annual symposium devoted to issues related to North American integration. The theme of the November 1992 conference in Mérida will be "Sustainable Integration: How Far? How Fast?"

RESOURCES

- *PROFMEX Monograph Series* published through the University of Arizona.
- *Mexico Policy News*. PROFMEX newsletter published through San Diego State University.
- *PROFMEX Special Papers Series* published through the University of Texas at El Paso.
- Joint papers with Universidad Autónoma Metropolitana — Azcapotzalco.
- *Reciprocal Images. Education in U.S. Mexican Relations/Imágenes recíprocas. La educación en las relaciones México-Estados Unidos de América*, edited by Paul Ganster and Mario Miranda Pacheco. Proceedings of the Fifth PROFMEX-ANUIES Conference in 1988. Universidad Autónoma Metropolitana — Azcapotzalco. 355 pages. 1991.
- *El Acuerdo de Libre Comercio México-Estados Unidos y repercusiones en la frontera*, by Eugenio O. Valenciano with the collaboration of Paul Ganster. Buenos Aires para la Integración en América Latina/BIDINTAL. 1991. 50 pages.

OTHER OFFICES

Mexico Policy News
Paul Ganster, Editor
Institute for Regional Studies of the Californias (IRSC)
San Diego State University
San Diego, CA 92182-0435
Phone: (619) 594-5423
Fax: (619) 594-5474

PROFMEX Presidency
James W. Wilkie, President
UCLA Program on Mexico
Los Angeles, CA 90024
Phone: (310) 454-8812
Fax: (310) 454-3109

Secretaría General de PROFMEX
Edmundo Jacobo Molina, Secretario
Universidad Autónoma Metropolitana
Contact: Arturo Grunstein, Secretario Adjunto
Phone: (5) 5-89-07-42/57-67-08
Fax: (5) 3-95-39-02

Office of Policy Studies
Ronald G. Hellman, Director
Bildner Center
Graduate Center
City University of New York
33 W. 42nd St.
New York, NY 10036
Phone: (212) 642-2950
Fax: (212) 642-2789

Office of Policy Linkages
Rafael Fernández de Castro, Director
Departamento de Estudios Internacionales
Instituto Tecnológico Autónomo de México
Río Hondo No. 1
Col. San Angel 01000
México, D.F.
Phone: (5) 5-48-24-41
Fax: (5) 5-50-76-37

Office of Membership and Canadian Exchanges
John H. Coatsworth, Director
Mexican Studies Program
University of Chicago
5848 S. University Ave.
Chicago, IL 60637
Phone: (312) 702-8395
Fax: (312) 702-7550

Office of Special Papers Series and Mexican Exchanges
Samuel Schmidt, Director
Center for Inter-American and Border Studies
University of Texas
El Paso, TX 79968
Phone: (915) 747-5196
Fax: (915) 747-5574

Office of Electronic Networking
José Warman, Director
CETEI-UNAM, Camino Real a Xochimilco 60
Tepepan, Xochimilco
México, D.F. 16020
Phone: (5) 6-75-30-01
Fax: (5) 6-75-44-84

Office of Monograph Series
Michael C. Meyer, Editor
Oscar J. Martínez, Associate Editor
Latin America Area Center
University of Arizona
Tucson, AZ 85721
Phone: (602) 621-7106
Fax: (602) 621-9424

Office of Research & Development
James F. Platler, Director
21607 Rambla Vista Dr.
Malibu, CA 90265
Phone: (310) 456-5778
Fax: (310) 456-0093

Office of U.S.-Mexican Studies
David E. Lorey, Coordinator
UCLA Program on Mexico
Los Angeles, CA 90024
Phone: (310) 287-1626
Fax: (310) 206-3555

Visiting Scholars' Center in Mexico City
Francisco Marmolejo, Director
University of the Americas at Mexico City
Av. Chapultepec 372
México, D.F. 06700
Phone: (5) 2-08-68-23
Fax: (5) 2-98-96-85

Office in Canada
IBM Tower
Dominion Centre #300
Toronto, ON M5K 1N2
Phone: (416) 865-0040
Fax: (416) 865-7380
Contact: Alan S. Alexandroff

U.S.-Mexican Policy Studies Program

L.B. Johnson School of Public Affairs
University of Texas at Austin
PO Box 7819
Austin, TX 78713-7819
Phone: (512) 471-1835
Fax: (512) 471-8951
Contact: Sidney Weintraub

DESCRIPTION

This program focuses on binational trade, political change in Mexico, the free trade agreement, and border issues, such as environment, infrastructure, hazardous waste, *colonias*, water allocation, and health issues.

ACTIVITIES

The program co-sponsored an October 1991 Acapulco meeting to analyze the impact of free trade on the labor market in Mexico. It also examines issues related to trade between Texas and Mexico, and studies opposition governments in northern and central Mexico.

UCLA Program on Mexico*

Latin American Center
University of California, Los Angeles
11250 Bunche Hall
405 Hilgard Ave.
Los Angeles, CA 90024-1487
Phone: (310) 206-8500/825-0870
Fax: (310) 206-3555
Email: gibson@others.sscnet.ucla.edu
Contact: Dr. David E. Lorey

DESCRIPTION

The program coordinates research on Mexico, faculty exchanges, and Mexico-related activities at UCLA. Through joint efforts with scholars from UCLA, other U.S. universities, and Mexican institutions, the program supports research in several broad areas related to Mexican society, economy, and public policy.

ACTIVITIES

The Cycles and Trends in 20th Century Mexico project convenes UCLA faculty, U.S. and Mexican academics, leading Mexican and U.S. policymakers, and representatives from the private sector to examine problems of mutual concern to Mexico and the United States. This group of 80 scholars and policymakers represents 38 institutions.

The U.S.-Mexican Border project has a dual focus: Borderlands Atlas Project and BorderLine, a computerized bibliography of resources about the U.S.-Mexican border region. The Atlas Project will result in a multivolume *Atlas of the United States-Mexico Borderlands*.

Reading English for Science and Technology (REST), a research and development project based on a 1985 agreement with the Universidad de Guadalajara, creates model English-reading curricula for university students in science disciplines. A second project, the Guadalajara Spanish Language Program, addresses the specific linguistic and cultural needs of UCLA Chicano students, who study in Guadalajara under the program's auspices.

The Colloquia and Speakers Series brings together Mexicanists from throughout the campus and the Los Angeles area to share research findings and to discuss Mexican affairs. It also serves as a public forum in which distinguished Mexican and U.S. scholars, Mexican policymakers, and U.S. government officials involved with Mexico regularly speak to the UCLA community on vital policy and research topics.

LINKS

UCLA hosts the presidency of PROFMEX. The Program on Mexico also maintains close ties with UC MEXUS, and is currently in the final year of a three-year project funded by USIA for exchange of researchers between UCLA, UNAM, and UAM.

RESOURCES

- *United States-Mexico Border Statistics since 1900*, edited by David E. Lorey. Statistics and interpretation on all aspects of the society and economy of the border region. UCLA Latin American Center Publications. 1990.
- *La crisis y reconversión industrial en México*, edited by Jesús Reyes Heroles and James W. Wilkie. The results of the three-year Hewlett Foundation-funded project titled U.S.-Mexico Social, Economic, and Technological Relations. In press at Universidad Autónoma Metropolitana — Azcapotzalco.

UC MEXUS (University of California Consortium on Mexico and the United States)*

Universitywide Headquarters
Riverside, CA 92521
Phone: (714) 787-3519
Fax: (714) 787-3856
Contact: Arturo Gomez-Pompa, Director

DESCRIPTION

As a consortium of the nine state-university campuses, UC MEXUS facilitates, supports, and promotes University of California activities in the subject areas of Mexican studies, U.S.-Mexico relations, and Chicano studies. It also encourages collaborative research between U.S. and Mexican scientists as well as scholarships in the arts and humanities as they relate to Mexico-U.S. relations and Mexican-origin populations in the United States.

ACTIVITIES

UC MEXUS sponsored a June 1992 international conference entitled "Myths in U.S.-Mexican Relations."

RESOURCES

- *UC MEXUS NEWS*. Quarterly newsletter. Free.

Udall Center for Studies in Public Policy*

University of Arizona
803/811 E. 1st St.
Tucson, AZ 85719
Phone: (602) 621-7189
Fax: (602) 621-9234
Contact: Robert G. Varady, Associate Director

DESCRIPTION

The center sponsors policy-relevant research and forums that link scholarship with decisionmaking. It also examines the policy formulation process and specializes in issues concerning the environment and natural resources, regional economic development, and health care. Reflecting its location in the Southwestern United States, the center has relied on the following logic: identify the major issues affecting the region, select timely subjects for consideration, generate ideas for specific projects, respond to initiatives, rely on a binational (U.S.-Mexico) network of researchers, and only then undertake appropriate programs.

ACTIVITIES

U.S.-Mexico Transboundary Water Resources Management: Bilateral Issues, Policies, and Strategies in the Nogales Area. This project, launched in mid-1989, has been undertaken jointly with two Mexican institutions, Colegio de la Frontera Norte and Instituto Tecnológico de Sonora, and with a team of University of Arizona scholars representing different disciplines. The project has enabled the Udall Center to participate actively in a real, evolving border issue. One useful output is a series of "borderless" maps showing physical, infrastructural and socioeconomic features. From this foundation, the center has extended its interest to the potential environmental consequences of a likely free trade agreement between Mexico and the United States.

To complement its research, the center seeks to inform policymakers by participating in the Integrated Environmental Plan for the Mexico-U.S. Border Area. In an attempt to incorporate grassroots ideas and sentiments, the center's 1991 Earth Day conference, subtitled "Bringing It Home," examined the Sonora bioregion. Also in 1991 the conference "The Treasures of the Sierra Madre" addressed a controversial World Bank-supported forestry development scheme south of the U.S. border. Representatives of community associations, Native American groups, and nongovernmental organizations shared a neutral forum with Mexican officials, World Bank representatives, and academic specialists.

RESOURCES

- *Preserving Arizona's Environmental Heritage*. Research report that identifies and discusses key environmental challenges facing the public and the state's decision-makers and provides policy options. Five of the volume's 16 chapters address binational issues affecting Arizona's border environment.
- *Border Issue Series*. This series of papers comprises three volumes. The first presents a historic overview of U.S.-Mexican relations, a theoretical paper on political-economic change, and an examination of political activism along the Texas border. The second collection examines the economic consequences of the 1986 Immigration Reform and Control Act, and analyzes differing perspectives of culture and politics in the borderlands. The third volume discusses the phenomenon of *colonias* in Texas. The center is also collaborating with Colegio de la Frontera Norte (COLEF) to publish a paper by a COLEF faculty member on trade unionism in the export-assembly industry.
- *Policy Currents*. Quarterly newsletter for the Public Policy Section of the American Political Science Association. Volume 2, Number 1, February 1992 includes *The Present Status of U.S.-Mexico Borderlands Studies, A Critique*, by Stephen P. Mumme, Vice-President, Association of Borderlands Scholars.
- *Maquila Impacts: Regional Perspectives*, edited by Arthur L. Silvers and Vera K. Pavlakovic. Includes essays on issues that impact on the border economy, labor, and environment.

PART VI

Government Agencies

INTRODUCTION

As the process of North American economic integration inches forward, it is spurred by forceful prods from government agencies in Canada, Mexico, and the United States. Interagency teams in the three countries are hammering out a series of agreements that will form the framework for a new trade and investment regime to govern North American economic relations. The dominant features of that new regime may soon be bound into an overarching North American free trade accord. The possibility that such an agreement might be signed has prompted a flurry of intergovernmental connections and joint operations over the past few years. But even if NAFTA does not win acceptance among the populations or policymakers of the three countries, the government agencies of North America will continue formulating strategies and building the international economic structures needed to facilitate integration.

In contrast to many organizations in the private sector, there is much more interest at the government level in promoting business links than in furthering other forms of social integration. But government agencies are also creating guidelines regarding immigration, the environment, labor, and other issues that accompany commercial integration. Most of the discussions on these issues are bilateral, with agreements emerging between pairs of countries rather than among all three. And in each of these discussions, the United States dominates due to its massive resource base and its extensive previous ties to Mexico and Canada. Prior to the NAFTA talks, Canada and Mexico had relatively few relations. Even with NAFTA, there will likely be few volatile issues—such as drug trafficking and immigration—occupying their binational foreign policy agenda.

Differences in the governmental systems in each country affect the style of negotiations about trade and other issues related to integration. Mexico's highly centralized system contrasts with a sharply decentralized system in the United States. The Mexican government is thus more single-minded about many of its positions, while the United States is more prone to pushing and tugging among different elements in the federal structure. Canada, with its federal structure and parliamentary system, lies somewhere between these two extremes, in part because of its more disciplined political parties. At the federal level in Canada, both the Standing Committee on Internal and External Affairs of the House of Commons and the Senate's Foreign Affairs Committee have been holding hearings on NAFTA, the proceeds of which are publicly available at the local level. Each Canadian province has a ministry, dealing with trade and development issues, monitoring NAFTA as well. In the United States, congressional committees have jurisdiction in almost every conceivable arena of cross-border relations. These committees write laws and oversee government programs that affect the character and pace of North American integration. Among these are the agriculture, banking, education and labor, energy and commerce, foreign affairs, judiciary, and ways and means committees in the House of Representatives. The finance and foreign relations committees are influential in the Senate. At the same time, state governments in both Mexico and the United States are, like the Canadian provinces, creating their own transborder links and conducting an increasing number of cooperative projects with their counterparts across the border.

In both Mexico and the United States, changes in governing structures may affect various initiatives, including NAFTA negotiations and implementation. Some elements of the Mexican government are being parceled out or restructured, including ministries responsible for important bilateral activities, such as the former environment ministry. Many of their functions are being folded into new "superministries," intended to be more efficient and streamlined. It is unclear how broad-ranging such changes will be or what effect they will have on future bilateral or trilateral activities.

Similarly, U.S. elections scheduled for November 1992 will decide the composition of the Congress as well as the presidency of the country. Both of the major presidential contenders favor NAFTA, but the elections could also result in changes in the leadership of key congressional committees with jurisdiction over the trade talks. It is unlikely, however, that such changes would seriously threaten NAFTA. In fact, it is possible that many current congressional opponents of the accord may shift to a pro-NAFTA position following the elections because they no longer feel compelled to reassure or pacify their constituents.

This section of *Cross-Border Links* includes agencies and committees that either perform important activities relating to the negotiation and implementation of NAFTA, or that sponsor or oversee other significant cross-border initiatives. Most of the agencies described provide resources or services that might be helpful to the public. Not all such agencies are included, often because they failed to respond to our inquiries, but we made every effort to locate and describe those agencies responsible for critical decisions about these international affairs. The focus is primarily on Mexico because it is the introduction of Mexico into the North American free trade arena that has spurred such a proliferation of cross-border linkages and generated such widespread public interest at the grassroots level.

1. CANADA

Department of External Affairs and International Trade*

Latin American and Caribbean Bureau
Lester Pearson Bldg.
125 Sussex Dr.
Ottawa, ON K1A 0G2
Phone: (613) 996-4626/6547

DESCRIPTION

The Department of External Affairs and International Trade is the equivalent of the U.S. State Department. Its Latin American trade and political divisions (of Programs, of Relations, and of Trade Development) are responsible for political and trade policy formation via their recommendations to the Canadian administration. The department's main foreign sources of information are Canadian embassies abroad, but Canada's provinces also have some input. Through the Department of Industry, Science and Technology, which coordinates the provincial offices (usually staffed by personnel from the Ottawa central office), each province determines its respective trading needs.

RESOURCES

- Publications, reports, or speeches of government officials. For reports contact: Trade Communications Division, phone (613) 996-7415. For speeches contact: Foreign Policy Communications Division, phone (613) 992-0760.

OTHER OFFICES

Canadian Embassy in Mexico
Schiller 529
Col. Polanco
México, D.F. 11560
Phone: (5) 2-54-32-88
Fax: (5) 2-55-03-53

Canadian Embassy in the United States
501 Pennsylvania Ave. NW
Washington, DC 20001
Phone: (202) 682-1740
Fax: (202) 682-7726

Canadian Consulate General-Chicago
2 Prudential Plaza
180 N. Stetson Ave. #2400
Chicago, IL 60601
Phone: (312) 616-1860

Canadian Consulate General-Dallas
750 North St. Paul Street #1700
Dallas, TX 75201-3281
Phone: (214) 922-9806

Canadian Consulate General-Detroit
600 Renaissance Center #1100
Detroit, MI 48243-1704
Phone: (303) 567-2340

Canadian Consulate General-Los Angeles
300 S. Grand Ave. #1000
Los Angeles, CA 90071
Phone: (213) 687-7432

Canadian Consulate General-Minneapolis
701 Fourth Ave. South #900
Minneapolis, MN 55415-1899
Phone: (619) 333-4641

Canadian Consulate General-New York City
1251 Avenue of the Americas
Exxon Building, 16th Floor
New York, NY 10020-1175
Phone: (212) 768-2400

Canadian Consulate General-Seattle
412 Plaza 600, 6th and Stewart
Seattle, WA 98101-1286
Phone: (206) 443-1777

Department of Finance of Canada*

L'esplanade Laurier
140 O'Connor St.
Ottawa, ON K1A 0G5
Phone: (613) 992-1573
Fax: (613) 995-5176 (Minister of Finance)
Contact: Information Services and Media Relations Division

DESCRIPTION

The Department of Finance of Canada is roughly the equivalent of the Treasury in the United States or the Hacienda in Mexico. It is responsible for the government's fiscal policies and its national budget. Canada's Department of Finance, however, enjoys a larger role in trade-policy formulation than either its U.S. or Mexican counterparts. It further differs from the U.S. Treasury by having a separate Department of Revenue Collection. In addition to advising on domestic and international financial matters, Canada's Department of Finance actively participates in international negotiations (NAFTA, for example) regarding trade, finance, taxation, investment, antidumping regulations, economic development, etc., by providing negotiators for the different task forces. The two divisions most directly involved in international aspects of the Canadian economy are the Fiscal Policy and Economic Analysis Branch, and the International Trade and Finance Branch, the latter formulating Canada's domestic and international trade policy.

Environment Canada*

International Affairs Directorate
10 Wellington St., #5
Hull, QB K1A 0H3
Phone: (819) 994-5147
Fax: (819) 953-7025
Contact: Lynn Berthiaume

DESCRIPTION

Environment Canada is the federal government department responsible for the environment, corresponding to the EPA (U.S.) and SEDESOL (Mexico) with whom it interacts. In fact, Environment Canada assists the Mexican government in monitoring and complying with environmental laws, some of which are the result of NAFTA negotiations, while others are the subject of outgrowths of parallel environmental projects between the two countries. Environment Canada is also preparing an Environmental Impact Statement regarding NAFTA.

2. MEXICO

Instituto Nacional de Estadística, Geografía, e Informática (INEGI)

Balderas 71
Col. Centro
México, D.F. 06040
Phone: (5) 5-54-16-13/14-95/19-05

DESCRIPTION

Despite its role as the main government clearinghouse for statistical information about Mexico, INEGI's information is not easily accessible. Its English-language publication has been discontinued and information is available only by visiting an INEGI office in person. INEGI information includes contemporary statistics on trade, employment, the economy, business, industry, and geography; national surveys on income, urban employment, etc; and a statistical agenda. INEGI has 4 branch offices in Mexico City, with further branches in Aguascalientes, Durango, Guadalajara, Hermosillo, Mérida, Monterrey, Oaxaca, Puebla, San Luis Potosí, and Toluca.

OTHER OFFICES

INEGI-Guadalajara
Ave. Alcalde 788
Sector Hidalgo
Guadalajara, Jal. 44280
Phone: (36) 14-07-99/19-09
Fax: (36) 13-10-67

INEGI-Hermosillo
Periférico Pte. 310
Edificio Ocotillo Business Park
Col. Las Quintas
Hermosillo, Son. 83240
Phone: (62) 16-10-33/20-76
Fax: (62) 16-07-63

INEGI-Monterrey
Ave. Eugenio Garza Sada 1702 Sur
Col. Nuevo Repueblo
Monterrey, N.L. 64700
Phone: (83) 72-52-34
Fax: (83) 45-01-98

Secretaría de Comercio y Fomento Industrial (SECOFI)

Alfonso Reyes 30, piso 10
Col. Hipódromo Condesa
México, D.F. 06179
Phone: (5) 2-86-17-57
Fax: (5) 2-86-15-43
Contact: Joaquín Gasca Salas, Director of Social Communication

DESCRIPTION

Secretaría de Comercio y Fomento Industrial (the Secretariat of Trade and Industrial Promotion) is responsible for implementing foreign-investment regulations and programs. Within SECOFI, the National Council for Foreign Investment (CNIE) and the National Register for Foreign Investment (RNIE) process all proposals for foreign investment in Mexico. Staff at the CNIE work closely with interested investors to expedite the investment permit process. SECOFI's head is Mexico's trade minister and as such oversees the country's negotiating team on NAFTA, but allegedly with little discretionary authority. President Salinas, Cabinet Coordinator José Córdoba, and Treasury Secretary Pedro Aspe apparently determine most negotiating goals and strategies.

ACTIVITIES

SECOFI has formed the Consejo Asesor del Tratado de Libre Comercio (Free Trade Agreement Advisory Board). This consulting organization was created in order to poll and represent leaders of diverse social sectors who meet on a monthly basis to evaluate the current course of the NAFTA negotiations. Its president is Jaime Serra Puche, SECOFI's Secretary. SECOFI also compiles statistics about foreign investment in Mexico, but this information is largely inaccessible to the public. What data SECOFI will release can be obtained more easily through INEGI.

RESOURCES

- *Partners in Trade: A North American Free Trade Zone*. Brochure.
- Two dozen pamphlets on various aspects of free trade, from dispute resolution to the auto parts sector. These are only sporadically available.

OTHER OFFICES

Consejo Asesor del Tratado de Libre Comercio
Alfonso Reyes 30
Col. Hipodromo Condesa
Mexcio, D.F. 06179
Phone: (5) 2-86-04-94
Fax: (5) 2-86-25-43
Contact: Socorro Díaz Palacios, General Coordinator, or Rodolfo Camacho Anzola, Private Secretary.

Secretaría de Desarrollo Social (SEDESOL)
— see Addendum

Av. Constituyentes 947, Edif. B, planta baja
Col. Belén de las Flores
México, D.F. 01110
Phone: (5) 2-71-84-81/85-21
Fax: (5) 2-71-82-17

DESCRIPTION

Secretaría de Desarrollo Social (the Ministry of Social Development) was created in the Spring of 1992 as an amalgamation of several agencies and programs. It is responsible for environmental issues formerly covered by the Ministry of Urban Development and Ecology (SEDUE). As this directory goes to print, it is still unclear which of SEDUE's functions will remain with SEDESOL, and which will be spun off to "decentralized" commissions such as the new National Ecology Commission or the National Water Commission. Since SEDESOL is headed by Luis Donaldo Colosio (a top contender for the presidency in 1994), government attention to environmental issues will likely continue to be driven by political considerations.

Secretaría de Desarrollo Urbano y Ecología (SEDUE)
— see Addendum

Av. Constituyentes 947, Edif. B, planta baja
Col. Belén de las Flores
México, D.F. 01110
Phone: (5) 2-71-87-65/82-17
Fax: (5) 2-71-82-17
Contact: Director of Social Communication

DESCRIPTION

As noted above in the description of SEDESOL, SEDUE has been dismantled, its environmental functions divided among a variety of government agencies. SEDUE had only recently begun to implement its environmental mandate. In 1990 SEDUE began a series of joint projects with the U.S. Environmental Protection Agency (EPA). These included training programs, emergency response drills, industrial inspections, and an inventory of border environmental needs. It is not clear how any of these activities will be affected by the agency's reorganization or by its new leadership. We have listed the phone numbers of local offices of the former SEDUE in the expectation that they will be retained by the new agency, and that they can provide accurate local information.

ACTIVITIES

In 1991, SEDUE and EPA developed an Integrated Border Environmental Plan—largely an inventory of existing problems and projects. Partly in response to criticism that the plan was all talk and no action, SEDUE announced a three-year program for immediate action to address the most pressing environmental problems and strengthen the infrastructure along the border. The agency stated that it would spend approximately U.S. $460 million on waste water treatment, municipal solid waste, roads, and territorial reserves. In 1992, nine communities were slated to receive approximately U.S. $147 million.

RESOURCES

- *Integrated Environmental Plan for the Mexican-U.S. Border Area (First Stage, 1992-1994).* Edited by SEDUE and EPA.

- *Protecting the Environment: Mexico's Public Works Program for the Border Region.* Brochure.

OTHER OFFICES

SEDESOL-Ciudad Juarez
Parque del Chamizal
Ciudad Juárez, Chih.
Phone: (16) 13-36-32
Contact: Rosa Maria Salas, Subdelegada

SEDESOL-Laredo
Delegación Ciudad Victoria
Nuevo Laredo, Tamps.
Phone: (131) 2-68-22/45-08

SEDESOL-Mexicali
Palacio Federal Zdo. Nivel, cuerpo A
Centro Civico Comercial
Mexicali, B.C. 21000
Phone: (65) 56-07-01
Contact: Luis Lopez Moctezuma

Secretaría de Relaciones Exteriores

Ave. Ricardo Flores Magón 1, piso 19
Col. Guerrero
México, D.F. 06995
Phone: (5) 7-82-36-60/37-65
Fax: (5) 7-82-35-11
Contact: Carlos Reta Martínez, Director of Information

DESCRIPTION

Secretaría de Relaciones Exteriores (the Secretariat of Foreign Affairs), Mexico's lead agency for foreign policy development and implementation, is also charged with running the country's embassies and consulates. Although involved in the negotiation of NAFTA, it is not a principal player. The primary duty of the embassy and consulates is to protect the interests and rights of Mexican citizens in foreign countries.

ACTIVITIES

The Mexican embassy in Washington operates an Office for Free Trade Agreement Negotiations, which monitors U.S. politics and issues affecting NAFTA as well as aiding in Mexico's public relations effort. The office also organizes conferences and trips of Hispanic and American groups to Mexico. For their part, the Mexican consulates facilitate commercial trade, promote university exchanges, etc.

LINKS

The consulates coordinate their work with state and local governments and with the U.S. Immigration and Naturalization Service (INS).

RESOURCES

- *Information Packages* on the state of the Mexican economy and social conditions. Available free from the Embassy of Mexico.

OTHER OFFICES

Embassy of Mexico in the United States
Office for Free Trade Agreement Negotiations*
1776 'Eye' St. NW #820
Washington, DC 20006
Phone: (202) 728-1739/74
Fax: (202) 296-4904
Contact: Luis de la Calle

Mexican Consulate
300 N. Michigan Ave. #2
Chicago, IL 60601
Phone: (312) 855-1380/84

Mexican Consulate
610 A St. #1
San Diego, CA 92101
Phone: (619) 231-8427/23

Mexican Consulate
1349 Empire Central #100
Dallas, TX 75247
Phone: (214) 630-7341/43

Mexican Consulate
2401 W. 6th St.
Los Angeles, CA 90057
Phone: (213) 351-6800
Fax: (213) 389-9186

Mexican Consulate
127 Navarro St.
San Antonio, TX 78205
Phone: (512) 227-9145/46

Mexican Consulate
8 E. 41st St.
New York, NY 10017
Phone: (212) 689-0456/58

Mexican Consulate
4200 Montrose Blvd. #120
Houston, TX 77006
Phone: (713) 524-2300/4861

Mexican Consulate
910 E. San Antonio St.
El Paso, TX 79901
Phone: (915) 533-3634/3645

Mexican Consulate
1612 Farragut St.
Laredo, TX 78040
Phone: (512) 723-0990/6369

Mexican Consulate
1990 W. Camelback #110
Phoenix, AZ 85015
Phone: (602) 242-7398
Fax: (602) 242-2957

3. UNITED STATES

Agency for International Development (AID)

320 21st St. NW
Washington, DC 20523
Phone: (202) 647-4359
Fax: (202) 647-4790
Contact: Arthur Danart, Mexico Desk

DESCRIPTION

AID is the branch of the U.S. State Department responsible for promoting development in foreign countries. The agency classifies Mexico as an advanced developing country. AID/Mexico goals include increased trade and investment ties, enhanced links between U.S. and Mexican organizations and increased Mexican use of U.S. technology. Passage and successful implementation of NAFTA are new goals for AID in Mexico.

ACTIVITIES

In Mexico, AID concentrates on training, technical assistance, information dissemination, and educational exchanges. The agency's major project areas in Mexico include: environment and conservation, food assistance, population control, health and child survival, narcotics-demand reduction, AIDS, and private-enterprise development. It also provides NAFTA-related training and technical assistance to Mexican agencies. Other NAFTA-related projects include: advising Mexican businesses on ways to respond to new environmental standards; developing labor standards concerning child labor, health and safety, dispute resolution, and collective bargaining; trade promotion; helping Mexico meet U.S. conservation standards for shrimp and tuna fishing; and working with SECOFI to develop standards on intellectual property rights. The agency also encourages bilateral relationships through assistance to Mexican nongovernmental organizations as well as government agencies for cooperative projects with or technical assistance from U.S. counterparts.

California Governor's Office of California - Mexico Affairs*

1350 Front St. #6054
San Diego, CA 92101
Phone: (619) 525-4641
Fax: (619) 525-4640
Contact: Elsa Saxod, Director

DESCRIPTION

As a liaison, this office serves as the focal point of California's official activities with Mexico.

ACTIVITIES

The office represents the U.S. side on the Commission of the Californias, which also includes representatives from the states of Baja California and Baja California Sur in Mexico. In addition, the office provides staff support for the California delegation to the Border Governor's Conference. Held annually, the conference includes representatives from the governors' offices in all ten border states (six on the Mexico side and four in the United States). Both the commission and the conference maintain working committees with staffs drawn from both sides of the border. These committees study bilateral issues and report to their respective bodies. The border governors then use the committee reports to make recommendations to the presidents of each country or to develop state policies.

RESOURCES

- *Joint Communique Signed by the Governors of the United States-Mexico Border States at the 10th Border Governors' Conference*, April 3, 1992. The communique may be requested through the California office or through the office of any border state in the United States or Mexico.

OTHER OFFICES

California Governor's Office of International Affairs
State of California
1400 Tenth St. #109
Sacramento, CA 95814
Phone: (916) 445-2841
Contact: Francisco R. Herrera, Assistant to the Governor for International Affairs

California Office of Trade and Investment in Mexico

Paseo de la Reforma 450, piso 4
Col. Juárez
México, D.F. 06600
Phone: (5) 2-08-51-61
Fax: (5) 2-08-57-61
Contact: Carlos Valderrama, Director

California State World Trade Commission*

1121 L St. #310
Sacramento, CA 95814
Phone: (916) 324-5511
Fax: (916) 324-5791
Contact: Gregory Mignano

DESCRIPTION

The commission is the export-development arm of the state of California. As such, it promotes policies and programs that improve California's ability to export goods and services.

Department of Agriculture (USDA)

Area Office for Mexico
FAS/FAA #5092
South Building
Washington, DC 20250-1000
Phone: (202) 720-3221
Fax: (202) 720-6063
Contact: Steve Huete

DESCRIPTION

USDA is the agency of the U.S. government responsible for promoting U.S. exports of agricultural commodities and for advising U.S. policymakers about foreign agricultural and trade policies. It is a participant in the NAFTA negotiations and is represented on the Trade Policy Review Group, an undersecretary-level body involved in decisionmaking regarding NAFTA. Two USDA agencies, the Foreign Agricultural Service (FAS) and the Commodity Credit Corporation (CCC) provide an assortment of export-promotion services designed to stimulate Mexico's demand for U.S. agricultural commodities.

ACTIVITIES

The agricultural affairs office at any U.S. embassy coordinates in-country representation of U.S. agroindustry interests. The office provides information on market factors and trends to U.S. exporters to help them capitalize on foreign market opportunities. Agricultural officers also report on agricultural and trade policies of the host country and their implications for U.S. exporters. USDA offers GSM-102 and GSM-103 credit guarantee programs to finance exports of U.S. commodities. FAS also conducts a variety of market-development programs to help U.S. exporters enter the Mexican market.

RESOURCES

- A wide variety of publications designed to promote U.S. agricultural exports are available from the USDA. Contact Dale Good, Reports Officer. Phone: (202) 720-8924; fax: (202) 720-7729 for titles and subscription information.
- *Trade Information Contacts* lists names, phone, and fax numbers of people involved in U.S.-Mexico agricultural trade. Report No. MX-2112. May 19, 1992.
- *Guidebook for Exporting U.S. Agricultural Products to Mexico*. Office of the Counselor for Agricultural Affairs. Available Summer 1992.
- "Mexico: The Market for U.S. Food and Farm Products," *FAS Market Profile*, May 1990.

OTHER OFFICES

Office of the Counselor for Agricultural Affairs
U.S. Embassy, Mexico City
PO Box 3087
Laredo, TX 78044
Phone: (5) 2-11-00-42
Telex: 017-73-091
Fax: (5) 5-33-61-94
Contact: Varies depending on agricultural product

Department of Commerce*

International Trade Administration
U.S. and Foreign Commercial Service (US&FCS)
Washington, DC 20230
Phone: (202) 377-2736
Fax: (202) 377-3159
Contact: Brian Smith

DESCRIPTION

The Commerce Department is the U.S. government agency with primary responsibility for fostering foreign and domestic commerce. Through its various divisions, the department engages in NAFTA negotiations. With its Mexican counterpart, the Commerce Department also participates in the Joint Committee on Investment and Trade, a bilateral body set up in 1989 to identify and promote commercial relations between the two countries.

The International Trade Administration is the branch of the Commerce Department responsible for various aspects of U.S. trade promotion and regulation as well as administration of U.S. trade laws. Its Office of Mexico has two components: the trade policy division and the commercial programs division. The trade policy division aims to reduce trade barriers and promote open markets. The commercial programs division provides business counseling, conducts outreach activities to businesses seeking to engage in international commerce, sponsors conferences, and conducts business development missions overseas.

The U.S. and Foreign Commercial Service (US&FCS) is the field component of the International Trade Administration. It promotes U.S. exports and provides services to U.S. firms wishing to do business in foreign countries. It also staffs U.S. embassies with commercial officers and operates the U.S. Trade Center in Mexico City.

ACTIVITIES

Services of the Foreign Commercial Service in Mexico include trade missions and shows, "matchmaker" events and services, and market research. US&FCS also helps settle trade and investment disputes between U.S. firms and Mexican enterprises. General export-support services are free of charge and include consultations with US&FCS staff as well as use of directories or of the data base in the Commercial Library at the Trade Center. Other support services are available for a fee and are tailored to the needs of the individual firm. Such services may include market briefings, surveys of potential representatives or customers, prearranged appointments, use of an interpreter/secretary, and office space.

The Trade Center in Mexico City organizes and promotes monthly industry-specific trade shows, as well as a multi-industry show called Rep-Com, aimed at small- and medium-size U.S. and Mexican companies. The center also provides space for business-sponsored promotional programs, during which eligible U.S. businesses and their Mexican subsidiaries or representatives rent exhibition and meeting space for their own events.

The Trade Information Center in Washington, DC, provides general information on export promotion, export procedure, and federal government programs designed to assist exporters.

RESOURCES

- *Overseas Business Reports*. Periodical of the International Trade Administration.
- "Marketing in Mexico," *Overseas Business Reports* (August 1990).

- *U.S. Exports to Mexico: A State-by-State Overview, 1987-1990* (Washington: International Trade Administration, August 1991).
- "North American Free Trade Negotiations: Most Frequently Asked Questions and Their Answers," (Washington: Department of Commerce, February 14, 1991).
- National Trade Data Base. Contains worldwide trade information, collected on an annual basis and stored on computer disk. Access to the data base is through regional depository libraries in the United States, as well as through other outlets. Call 1-800-USA Trade for information about location of data base. Also available by subscription. $350/yr.
- US&FCS publishes current reports on promising sectors for U.S. exports, covering market size, contacts, duties, and forecasts. $10 per report.
- US&FCS publishes lists of key companies and contacts for exporters. $50 per sector.

OTHER OFFICES

Representatives of the Commerce Department are located in various cities throughout the United States, Mexico, and Canada. Local staff can help set up business development missions, provide information about conferences, and advise about market conditions and opportunities. Find local offices by contacting 1-800-USA Trade within the United States.

Office of Mexico
Room 3022
Washington, DC 20230
Phone: (202) 377-4464
Fax: (202) 377-5865
Contact: Ted Johnson

Office of Canada
Room 3033
Washington, DC 20230
Phone: (202) 377-3101
Fax: (202) 377-3718
Contact: Kathleen Keim

Each of the following addresses is preceded by:

U.S. Department of Commerce
International Trade Administration
U.S. & Foreign Commercial Service
Overseas Commercial Section

U.S. Embassy - Mexico City
Paseo de la Reforma 305
México, D.F. 06500
U.S. mailing address: PO Box 3087
Laredo, TX 78044-3087
Phone: (5) 2-11-00-42
Fax: (5) 2-07-89-38
Contact: Carlos Poza

American Consulate General - Guadalajara
Progreso 175
Guadalajara, Jal.
U.S. mailing address: PO Box 3098, Laredo, TX 78044-3098
Phone: (3) 6-25-03-21
Fax: (3) 6-26-35-76
Contact: Americo Tadeu

American Consulate General - Monterrey
Ave. Constitución 411 Poniente
Monterrey, N.L.
U.S. mailing address: PO Box 3098, Laredo, TX 78044-3098
Phone: (8) 3-45-21-20
Fax: (8) 3-42-51-72
Contact: Dawn Cooper-Bahar

U.S. Embassy - Ottawa
100 Wellington St.
Ottawa, ON
U.S. mailing address: PO Box 5000, Ogdensburg, NY 13669
Phone: (613) 238-5335
Fax: (613) 233-8511
Contact: Robert Marro

American Consulate General - Calgary
815 MacLeod Trail SE #1000
Calgary, AE
U.S. mailing address: c/o U.S. Embassy - Ottawa, PO Box 5000, Ogdensburg, NY 13669
Phone: (403) 265-2116
Fax: (403) 264-6630
Contact: Commercial Officer

American Consulate General - Halifax
Cogswell Tower #910
Scotia Square
Halifax, NS B3J 3K1
U.S. mailing address: c/o U.S. Embassy - Ottawa, PO Box 5000, Ogdensburg, NY 13669
Phone: (902) 429-2482
Fax: (902) 423-6861
Contact: Richard Vinson

American Consulate General - Montreal
South Tower #1122
Place Desjardins
Montreal, PQ
U.S. mailing address: PO Box 847, Champlain, NY 12919-0847
Phone: (514) 398-9895
Fax: (514) 398-0711
Contact: Geoffrey Walser

American Consulate General - Toronto
480 University Ave., Ste. 602
Toronto, ON
U.S. mailing address: PO Box 135, Lewiston, NY 14092
Phone: (416) 595-5413
Fax: (416) 595-5419
Contact: Dan Wilson

American Consulate General - Vancouver
1095 West Pender St. #20
Vancouver, BC
U.S. mailing address: PO Box 5002, Point Roberts, WA 98281
Phone: (604) 685-3382
Fax: (604) 685-5285
Contact: Stephen Wasylko

Commercial Library
U.S. Trade Center
Liverpool 31
Col. Juárez
México, D.F. 06600
Phone: (5) 2-11-00-42 ext. 3281

Promotion Office
Calle Allende #3330
Col. Jardín
Nuevo Laredo, Tamps. 88260
U.S. mailing address: Drawer 3089, Laredo, TX 78044-3089

Trade Information Center
14th and Constitution Ave. NW
Washington, DC 20230
Phone (within the U.S.): 1-800-USA Trade

Department of Labor/Bureau of International Labor Affairs

200 Constitution Ave. NW #S-5325
Washington, DC 20210
Phone: (202) 219-6274
Fax: (202) 219-9074
Contact: Gregory K. Schoepfle, Director of Foreign Economic Research

DESCRIPTION

The Department of Labor is the U.S. government agency responsible for setting and enforcing U.S. labor laws, measuring the impact of U.S. policies on labor, and helping to devise official policies regarding labor in the United States. The department is a participant in the Trade Policy Review Group and took part in "parallel track" negotiations regarding labor issues that were conducted simultaneously with the NAFTA talks. The foreign economic research program of the department's Bureau of International Labor Affairs evaluates potential effects of U.S. international economic policies and foreign economic developments on the earnings and employment of U.S. workers. The bureau's research arm often responds to requests from Congress or executive branch agencies. Research topics include analysis of changes in international trade, investment, and technology transfer.

ACTIVITIES

North American economic relations were a priority area for the bureau's research studies during 1991. Studies assessed the effects of NAFTA on U.S. labor, labor-management relations and job restructuring in the North American automobile industry, and labor issues related to export-oriented assembly and processing operations in Mexico and the Caribbean. The foreign economic research office prepared background papers for the fast-track consideration of NAFTA and for the Department of Labor's discussions with its Mexican counterpart, the Mexican Secretariat of Labor and Social Welfare. The department has a memorandum of understanding with the its counterpart to implement a number of joint projects relating to bilateral trade and labor issues.

RESOURCES

- *Economic Discussion Paper* series. A wide range of contract research reports, published articles, and in-house studies. A complete list of publications may be requested from the Bureau of International Labor Affairs, Office of International Economic Affairs. Following is a selected sample of titles:
- "Labor Issues Related to a U.S.-Mexico FTA: A View from the North," October 1991.
- "Research Summary: *Industrial Effects of a Free Trade Agreement Between Mexico and the USA* by Interindustry Economic Research Fund, Inc.," March 12, 1991.
- "The North American Auto Industry at the Onset of Continental Free Trade Negotiations," *Economic Discussion Paper #38*, November 1991.
- "Continental Integration and the Future of the North American Auto Sector," October 1991.
- "U.S.-Mexico Free Trade Agreement: The Maquilazation of Mexico?" April 18, 1990.
- "Implications for U.S. Employment of the Recent Growth in Mexican Maquiladoras," by Gregory K. Schoepfle in *Revista Frontera Norte*, January-June 1991.
- "The North American Free Trade Agreement: Comparisons with and Lessons from Southern EC Enlargement," *Economic Discussion Paper #39*, November 1991.
- "Trade-Sensitive U.S. Industries: Employment Trends and Worker Characteristics," *Economic Discussion Paper #36*, July 1991.
- "Labor Standards in Export Assembly Operations in Mexico and the Caribbean," June 1990.
- "Worker Rights in Export Processing Zones: Mexico," August 1990.

Environmental Protection Agency (EPA)

401 M St. NW
Washington, DC 20406
Phone: (202) 260-4890
Contact: Sylvia Correa

DESCRIPTION

The EPA is responsible for enforcing U.S. laws regarding environmental protection. Primarily a domestic agency, the EPA has become involved in a variety of binational projects with Mexico. The increased binational cooperation of the EPA with its Mexican counterparts dates from 1983 and the signing of the "La Paz Agreement" by presidents Ronald Reagan and Miguel de la Madrid. Since then, there have been seven U.S.-Mexico environmental agreements, but the number of joint projects and the extent of cooperation escalated sharply after the decision was made to pursue free trade negotiations. The EPA is a participant in "parallel track" negotiations on environmental protection being conducted concurrent with negotiations regarding NAFTA.

ACTIVITIES

Mexico is the site of the EPA's first-ever representative abroad, and an EPA environmental attaché is currently stationed at the U.S. embassy in Mexico City. The attaché assists, counsels, and serves as a liaison between the U.S. and Mexican governments. The EPA and Mexico are involved in joint projects regarding environmental issues both in Mexico City and in the border area. The EPA and its Mexican counterpart, SEDUE, drafted an integrated environmental plan for the U.S.-Mexico border focusing on issues such as water quality, hazardous wastes, air quality, and chemical emergencies. With the U.S. Trade Representative's office and other U.S. agencies, the EPA compiled an "Environmental Review Document" analyzing the environmental effects of a free trade agreement. With Mexico, the EPA set up a bilateral Working Group on Enforcement to enhance efforts to enforce environmental regulations in both countries. The EPA, SEDUE, the Mexican electronics industry, Northern Telecom, and the Industry Cooperative on Ozone Protection collaborate through a technology transfer and information exchange program to help reduce use of agents that deplete the ozone layer. The EPA also provides training and technical assistance to Mexico for various environmental programs.

EPA Region IX is one of two regional departments of the EPA responsible for U.S.-Mexico environmental affairs. This department concentrates on California, Arizona, and counterpart states in Mexico. Region IX's Mexico Team includes representatives from the hazardous waste, air, and water divisions of the EPA in the region. The team oversees projects relating to shared U.S.-Mexico environmental concerns. Various projects are bilateral, including the hazardous waste division's Sister City Plan, an effort to devise joint response plans regarding potential hazardous waste spills for the 14 major border city pairs.

OTHER OFFICES

Environmental Protection Agency, Region IX
75 Hawthorne St.
San Francisco, CA 94105
Phone: (415) 744-1281
Fax: (415) 744-1072
Contact: Enrique Manzanilla, Regional Border Coordinator

Environmental Protection Agency, Region VI
1st Interstate Tower at Fountain Place
1455 Ross Ave #1200
Dallas, TX 75202-2733
Phone: (214) 655-2210
Fax: (214) 655-6648
Contact: Oscar Ramírez, U.S./Mexico Coordinator

General Accounting Office (GAO)*

PO Box 6015
Gaithersburg, MD 20877
Phone: (202) 275-6241

DESCRIPTION

The GAO is part of the legislative branch and directly supports the U.S. Congress by providing audits and evaluations of virtually every federal program, activity, and function—from health care to international trade. Through reports, testimony before Congress, legal opinions, and information briefings with congressional staff, the GAO provides information for congressional decisionmaking. The GAO's Headquarters Divisions are: Accounting and Financial Management; General Government; Human Resources; Information Management and Technology; National Security and International Affairs; Program Evaluation and Methodology; and Resources, Community, and Economic Development.

The GAO's Los Angeles Regional Office staff has performed numerous studies concerning U.S.-Mexico relations since 1989. Its studies have focused on agricultural trade, reform in Mexico's petrochemical industry, wages and fringe benefits, environmental regulation and enforcement, occupational safety and health, and the adequacy of border infrastructure.

GAO Los Angeles has 11 completed projects (and reports) and six ongoing projects related to U.S.-Mexico relations. Ongoing GAO assignments led by the Los Angeles Regional Office include: 1) Relocation of U.S. Firms to Mexico; 2) U.S.-Mexico Oil Trade and Investment Issues; 3) U.S.-Mexico Trade: Mexican Environmental Controls on New Companies; 4) U.S. Auto Parts Plants in Mexico; 5) North American Free Trade Agreement; and 6) U.S.-Chile Trade.

RESOURCES

- *Trends and Impediments in Agricultural Trade*. Briefing Report to the Chairman, Committee on Agriculture, House of Representatives. January 1990.
- *Extent to Which Mexican Horticultural Exports Complement U.S. Production*. Briefing Report to the Chairman, Committee on Agriculture, House of Representatives. March 1991.
- *Impact of Liberalization in the Agricultural Sector*. Report to the Chairman, Committee on Agriculture, House of Representatives. March 1991.
- *Occupational Safety and Health and Child Labor Policies of the United States and Mexico*. Testimony before the Subcommittee on Employment Opportunities and the Subcommittee on Labor-Management Relations, House of Representatives. April 1991.
- *Some U.S. Wood Furniture Firms Relocated from Los Angeles Area to Mexico*. Report to the Chairman, Committee on Energy and Commerce, House of Representatives. April 1991, and *El Traslado a México de Ciertos Fabricantes Estadounidenses de Muebles de Madera de la zona de Los Angeles*. April 1991.
- *Concerns About the Adequacy of Border Infrastructure*. Report to the Chairman, Committee on Finance, U.S. Senate. May 1991.
- *Information on Environmental Regulations and Enforcement*. Report to the Chairman, Committee on Commerce, Science and Transportation, U.S. Senate. May 1991. *Información acerca de la reglamentación ambiental y su cumplimiento*. May 1991.
- *The U.S. Reaction to Recent Reforms in Mexico's Petrochemical Industry*. Report to the Chairman, Subcommittee on International Economic Policy and Trade, Committee on Foreign Affairs, House of Representatives. May 1991.

- *Information on Wages, Fringe Benefits, and Workers Rights*. Report to the Chairman, Committee on Commerce, Science and Transportation, U.S. Senate. May 1991.
- *U.S. and Mexican Management of Hazardous Waste from Maquiladoras Hampered by Lack of Information*. Testimony before the Environment, Energy, and Natural Resources Subcommittee, Committee on Government Operations, House of Representatives. November 1991.
- *Survey of U.S. Border Infrastructure Needs*. Report to the Chairman, Committee on Finance, U.S. Senate. November 1991.

OTHER OFFICES

General Accounting Office-Los Angeles Regional Office International Group*
World Trade Center #1010
350 S. Figueroa St.
Los Angeles, CA 90071
Phone: (213) 346-8000
Fax: (213) 346-8142
Contact: Patrick Gormley, Program Manager

Illinois Trade Office in Mexico

Paseo de la Reforma 450, piso 4
Col. Juárez
México, D.F. 06600
Phone: (5) 2-08-97-87
Fax: (5) 5-11-20-84

Immigration and Naturalization Service (INS)*

U.S. Department of Justice
Washington, DC 20536
Phone: (202) 514-2648
Contact: Duke Austin, Director of Public Affairs

DESCRIPTION

An agency of the Justice Department, INS is responsible for enforcing U.S. immigration laws and administering procedures by which immigrants become U.S. citizens. The Border Patrol is the uniformed enforcement branch of INS and is primarily responsible for interdiction of undocumented immigrants, drug traffickers, and common criminals along U.S. borders between ports of entry.

ACTIVITIES

The bilateral activities of INS are focused on developing working relationships with Canadian and Mexican law enforcement agencies responsible for administration of immigration activities.

RESOURCES

- *INS Reporter*. Periodical. $10/yr.
- *INS Newsline*. Telephone-accessed information line about new policies, administrative changes, and news events at INS; normal long-distance charges apply. Phone: (202) 616-1994.

International Boundary and Water Commission, United States and Mexico*

U.S. Section
The Commons, Bldg. C #310
4171 N. Mesa St.
El Paso, TX 79902
Phone: (915) 534-6700
Fax: (915) 534-6680
Contact: Rene A. Valenzuela, Public Affairs Officer

DESCRIPTION

The mission of the International Boundary and Water Commission is to enforce the rights and obligations that the governments of the United States and Mexico assumed under numerous boundary and water agreements in a way that benefits the social, economic, and cross-boundary climate of the border region. The U.S. and Mexican sections maintain their respective headquarters in El Paso, Texas, and Ciudad Juárez, Chihuahua, with both nation's commissioners meeting at alternating offices. Each section maintains its own engineering staff and such legal advisers and other assistants as it deems necessary.

ACTIVITIES

The commission oversees binational allocation of the Rio Grande and Colorado rivers; regulation and conservation of the Rio Grande for use by the two countries through joint construction, operation and maintenance of international storage dams and hydroelectric plants; protection of lands along the rivers from floods by levee and floodway projects; solution of border sanitation and water quality problems; preservation of the Rio Grande as an international boundary; and demarcation of the land boundary.

OTHER OFFICES

International Boundary and Water Commission, United States and Mexico
Mexican Section
Av. Universidad 2180
Ciudad Juárez, Chih. 32320
Phone: (16) 13-73-63
Contact: Jesús Luévano

New Mexico Governor's Office*

Liaison for Border Development
State Capitol Bldg.
Santa Fe, NM 87503
Phone: (505) 827-3000
Fax: (505) 827-3026
Contact: John Garcia, Deputy Chief of Staff for the Governor

DESCRIPTION

This is New Mexico's top state office responsible for relations with Mexico and border development. Its focus is primarily on political relations with official representatives of Mexican federal, state, or local governments.

ACTIVITIES

The office represents New Mexico at the annual Border Governors' Conference. It loosely oversees the efforts of other state bodies involved in U.S.-Mexico activities, including the New Mexico Trade Division, the New Mexico Border Commission (a public relations group working with its Mexican counterpart to stimulate interest in tourism, trade, and investment), and the New Mexico Border Authority (which generates revenue for infrastructure development and other border-development needs).

RESOURCES

- *Joint Communique Signed by the Governors of the United States-Mexico Border States at the 10th Border Governors' Conference*, April 3, 1992. The communique may be requested through the New Mexico office or through the office of any border state in the United States or Mexico.

New Mexico Trade Division*

Economic Development Department
1100 St. Francis Dr.
Santa Fe, NM 87503
Phone: (505) 827-0309
Fax: (505) 827-0263
Contact: Roberto Castillo

DESCRIPTION

This is the division of the Economic Development Department of the state of New Mexico responsible for helping New Mexican businesses expand their operations outside of the state. Expanding trade with Mexico has become a high priority of the division due to the negotiation of NAFTA and the opening of a new commercial-quality border crossing in southern New Mexico.

ACTIVITIES

The division sponsors workshops and seminars worldwide on initiating trading relations with New Mexican businesses. It conducts monthly "*maquila* missions" in which interested New Mexican businesspeople tour *maquiladoras* and meet their purchasing agents with the goal of establishing commercial links between the companies. The division's "Border Trade Specialist," located in Las Cruces, New Mexico, acts as a matchmaker for businesses wishing to establish cross-border commercial links. The division will be opening a Mexico City trade office in 1992 to promote commerce, investment, and tourism between Mexico and New Mexico.

RESOURCES

- *Export Recap*. Annual publication focusing on New Mexico exports for the year. Free.
- *New Mexico Border Region: Zona de Oportunidad*. Periodical. Free.
- Various brochures available in a number of languages profile New Mexico commercial and industrial sectors. Free.

OTHER OFFICES

New Mexico Trade Division
Box 4298
Las Cruces, NM 88003
Phone: (505) 646-4249
Fax: (505) 646-6012
Contact: Robert Queen, Border Trade Specialist

Office of Technology Assessment (OTA)*

United States Congress
Washington, DC 20510-8025
Phone: (202) 228-6350
Fax: (202) 228-6344
Contact: Stephen A. Herzenberg

DESCRIPTION

The Office of Technology Assessment is an analytical support agency of the United States Congress. OTA works directly with and for the Committees of Congress, providing them with thorough analysis of technological issues. Governed by a 12-member, bipartisan congressional board—six senators and six representatives—and advised by a council of distinguished citizens, OTA operates with a multidisciplinary staff. In implementing its function, the office: 1) identifies existing or probable impacts of technology or technological programs; 2) ascertains, where possible, cause-and-effect relationships; and 3) identifies alternative technological methods of implementing specific programs.

ACTIVITIES

With its project on U.S.-Mexico Trade, Technology, and Investment, OTA examines the range of possible impacts on U.S. jobs and job opportunities, in terms of occupational categories and their skill requirements, as well as wage levels. OTA coordinates its assessment closely with GAO. OTA undertakes assessments at the request of the chairman of any congressional committee.

RESOURCES

- *U.S.-Mexico Trade, Technology, and Investment*. June 1992.
- *OTA reports, OTA publications list, OTA Annual report*. Free from OTA, (202) 224-8996.
- Reports and major background documents, including useful *contractor reports*, are available through the National Technical Information Service.

San Diego County Department of Transborder Affairs*

1600 Pacific Hwy. #273
San Diego, CA 92101
Phone: (619) 531-6489
Fax: (619) 531-5199
Contact: Augie Bareño

ACTIVITIES

The department provides administration, planning, research, evaluation, and resource-development services needed as a result of San Diego's position as a major urban border community. The department also works to develop cross-border partnerships among public, private, and academic organizations involved in transborder issues. It administers a variety of projects related to trade and economic development, health and environment, and public services. Its programs have focused on such issues as *maquiladora* impacts, trade zones, Pacific Rim strategies, binational health and sanitation issues, disaster preparedness, underage drinking, and immigration and migrant workers.

RESOURCES

- *Common Border—Shared Decisions?* Video. $15.
- *The Costs and Benefits of Immigration in the San Diego Region: The Need for a Local Response*. Report.
- *Cross Border Concerns in the San Diego Region: The Need for New Border Crossings*. Report.
- Maquiladora Fact Sheet.
- *A Public Meeting on the United States-Mexico Free Trade Negotiations*. Report.
- *Report on Border Related Activities Conducted by the County of San Diego*, submitted to the San Diego Association of Governments (SANDAG) Border Related Issues Task Force.

San Diego Mayor's Office of Binational Affairs*
— defunct (see Addendum)

202 C St., #11A
San Diego, CA 92101
Phone: (619) 236-6604
Fax: (619) 236-7228
Contact: Geoffrey Bogart, Director, or Geoffrey Land, Assistant Director

DESCRIPTION

The Mayor's Office of Binational Affairs was established in 1986 in response to heightened public awareness of the importance of U.S.-Mexico relations. The office functions as a liaison to local, state, and federal entities in both the United States and Mexico, concerning binational issues as well as responding to requests for information on binational and international issues. The office facilitates regional efforts to explore and understand the issues and opportunities in the U.S.-Mexico border region. Working closely with regional governments, research centers, private groups, and city officials, the office coordinates conferences, conducts public outreach, promotes cultural exchanges, and facilitates dialogue on a wide variety of binational issues. In association with various government and private groups in the United States and Mexico, the Office of Binational Affairs has addressed issues such as free trade, environmental protection, cultural affairs, education, immigration, disaster preparedness, and economic development.

ACTIVITIES

The office hosts and briefs visiting dignitaries and government representatives; hosts joint City Council meetings between the cities of San Diego and Tijuana; provides testimony before state and federal commissions on issues such as migration, infrastructure, *maquiladoras*, and border crossings; coordinates the Bilateral Working Group for the proposed TwinPorts airport at Otay Mesa; and participates in the Border Trade Alliance, serving on its infrastructure subcommittee. Furthermore, the Mayor's Office co-sponsored the 1991 Border Mayors Conference with the city of Tijuana; led a trade delegation to Mexico City to meet with high-level Mexican officials, including President Salinas; hosted and participated in the 1991 United States Trade Representative's public hearings in San Diego on NAFTA; and attended several industrial fairs.

Texas Department of Commerce*

PO Box 12728
Austin, TX 78711
Phone: (512) 320-9669
Fax: (512) 320-9674
Contact: Deborah Hernández or Tom Stellman

DESCRIPTION

This state economic development agency promotes industrial development, trade, and tourism between Texas and Mexico.

ACTIVITIES

Its border development program helps Texas companies sell to *maquilas* and assists businesses that want to establish production-sharing operations. It also serves as staff to a Texas-Mexico authority advisory group and as the Texas component of the Border Governor's Group. Its Tourism Division has a two-nation vacation program.

Texas Trade Office in Mexico

A.P. 5-602
México, D.F. 06500
Phone: (5) 5-66-35-32
Fax: (5) 5-35-31-66

United Nations International Labor Organization

1828 L St. NW #801
Washington, DC 20036
Phone: (202) 653-7652
Fax: (202) 653-7687

U.S. Information Agency/U.S. Information Service (USIA)

Mexico Desk
301 4th St. SW
Washington, DC 20547
Phone: (202) 619-6835
Contact: Marjorie Harrison

DESCRIPTION

The USIA is responsible for promoting a positive image overseas of the United States and its foreign policies. The agency generates support for present and proposed U.S. policies among foreign audiences through publications, radio and television broadcasts, visitor exchanges, trainings, seminars, and educational opportunities. The USIA advises the president, State Department, National Security Council, and other key officials on the implications of foreign opinion for current and proposed U.S. policies. Its current major focuses in Mexico are the NAFTA and drug control, although other areas, such as political studies, communications, agriculture, cultural interchanges, and environmental issues are also subjects of agency programs.

ACTIVITIES

The agency conducts visitor exchanges through such initiatives as the Voluntary Visitor program, International Visitors program (IV), and Community Leader program. It sponsors many visitor exchanges promoting NAFTA and targeting academics, farmers, government officials, labor, business leaders, and financial and banking officials. Antinarcotics exchanges are also common, focusing especially on drug-abuse prevention and rehabilitation programs. IV participants are drawn from established or potential foreign leaders in government, politics, media, education, science, labor relations, and other fields. The Youth Programs Division funds visitor programs for graduate students, artists, youth leaders, and university students. The Community Leader program has facilitated exchanges of artists, musicians, educators, conservationists, athletic coaches, performing artists, trainers for microenterprise development, and others. The agency operates the Benjamin Franklin Library in Mexico City.

RESOURCES

USIA publications created for foreign audiences are not available for distribution in the United States, although interested individuals may study these publications at the USIA library in Washington. Publications regarding Mexico include:

- "*Wireless File*" news service.
- *Dialogue (Facetas)*. Quarterly.
- *Research Memorandum* and *Briefing Paper*.
- "Drugs Seen as High Priority and Growing Problem in Mexico; Drug Kings' Power, Failure of International Cooperation Blamed," *Research Memorandum*, January 22, 1990.
- "Mexicans Optimistic about 'Free Trade Agreement'; Large Majorities Favor U.S. Help in Mexico's Fight Against Narcotrafficking," *Research Memorandum*, December 6, 1990.
- "Increased Number of Mexicans See Drug Use Growing; Believe U.S. Doing Well in Drug Struggle; and Want to Cooperate with U.S.," *Research Memorandum*, December 31, 1990.
- "Mexicans Enthusiastic about 'Free Trade Agreement,' " *Research Memorandum*, February 13, 1991.

OTHER OFFICES

Bureau of Educational and Cultural Affairs
(same address as USIA)
Phone: (202) 619-4597

U.S. International Trade Commission (ITC)*

500 E St. SW
Washington, DC 20436
Phone: (202) 205-3223
Fax: (202) 205-2340
Contact: Clint Shiells (on NAFTA research)

DESCRIPTION

The ITC is an independent commission set up to provide advice and analysis on U.S. trade and trade policy. It is not attached to the U.S. executive branch, but responds to research needs and requests of official U.S. agencies. The commission shares responsibility with the International Trade Administration of the U.S. Department of Commerce for cases involving dumping and countervailing duties.

ACTIVITIES

The ITC is a member of the Trade Policy Review Group, and provides technical advice and assistance to the U.S. NAFTA negotiating team. The ITC conducts research on cross-border trade relations, policies in Mexico, and (using mathematical models) the probable effects of NAFTA. The commission also holds international conferences relating to NAFTA and other trade issues.

RESOURCES

- "Rules of Origin Issues Related to NAFTA and the North American Automotive Industry." *USITC Publication* #2460, November 1991.
- "Operation of the Trade Agreements Program, 42nd Report, 1990." *USITC Publication* #2403, July 1991.
- "The Likely Impact on the United States of a Free Trade Agreement with Mexico." *USITC Publication* #2353, February 1991.
- "Review of Trade and Investment Liberalization Measures by Mexico and Prospects for Future United States-Mexican Relations, Investigation No. 332-282, Phase I: Recent Trade and Investment Reforms Undertaken by Mexico and Implications for the United States." *USITC Publication* #2275, April 1990.
- "Review of Trade and Investment Liberalization Measures by Mexico and Prospects for Future United States-Mexican Relations, Investigation No. 332-282, Phase II: Summary of Views on Prospects for Future United States-Mexico Relations." *USITC Publication* #2326, October 1990.

U.S.-Mexico Commission for Educational and Cultural Exchange*

Benjamin Franklin Library
Londres 16
Col. Juárez
México, D.F. 06600
Phone: (5) 2-11-00-42 ext. 3473/74
Fax: (5) 2-08-89-43

DESCRIPTION

This binational commission was created to support and expand educational and cultural exchanges between Mexico and the United States. The agreement establishing the commission was signed in November 1990 at the Bush/Salinas summit in Monterrey. The commission's ten-member board is appointed jointly by the Mexican Foreign Minister and the U.S. ambassador to Mexico. The board is evenly divided between Mexican and U.S. members.

ACTIVITIES

The commission administers the Fulbright Scholarship program in Mexico, offering grants for faculty development, English language training, a multidisciplinary master's degree program, and postdoctoral research. The commission's "Fund for Culture" sponsors small grants (under $25,000) for nonacademic cultural exchanges in fields such as dance, translation, and library management. It also supports nondegree research in cultural scholarship and conferences on cultural themes. With the nonprofit Debt-for-Development Coalition, the commission designed a debt-swap program called "Debt for Science, Technology, and Human Resources" to support relevant research and exchanges between U.S. and Mexican universities.

LINKS

The commission is funded by the U.S. and Mexican governments, as well as by some private organizations such as the Rockefeller Foundation. The commission operates exchange programs formerly administered by the U.S. Information Agency. It is housed in the same building as USIA offices in Mexico City, maintaining direct connections with USIA but operating as a bilateral program.

U.S. Trade Representative (USTR)

600 17th St. NW
Washington, DC 20506
Phone: (202) 395-3230
Contact: Public Affairs Office

DESCRIPTION

The U.S. Trade Representative is the lead U.S. Agency involved in negotiations on foreign trade and investment, as well as heading the U.S. NAFTA negotiations team. The following policy advisory groups give feedback to the USTR on trade and investment policy: the Industry Policy Advisory Committee, the Advisory Committee for Trade Policy and Negotiations, the Services Policy Advisory Committee, the Investment Policy Advisory Committee, the Inter-Governmental Policy Advisory Committee, the Defense Policy Advisory Committee on Trade, and the Labor Advisory Committee for Trade.

PART VII

Business Groups

INTRODUCTION

With very few exceptions, business groups in the United States and Canada have been strong proponents of the current path of continental integration, and have lined up strongly in favor of NAFTA. These groups have provided a formidable lobbying force for both countries' administrations, funding economic studies and public relations campaigns.

The Mexican picture has been less clear due to the large proportion of businesses that relied on protectionism for survival. But by the 1990s most Mexican business groups had lined up behind NAFTA, and those that hadn't had lost much of their influence. In contrast, those groups supporting the free trade process have had unparalleled access to the Mexican negotiating team, directly participating in setting the country's objectives and strategies.

Cross-border links among business groups have a very different nature from those among labor and nongovernmental organizations. The difference is due to two factors: the existence of advanced business information networks that ensure a rapid diffusion of business perspectives across borders even in the absence of formal cross-border ties, and the multinational nature of individual corporations.

The groups listed in this directory have been included either for their potential as a source of information or for their importance in setting the terms of the domestic and international debate over integration.

1. CANADA

Business Council for Fair Trade*

298 Garry St.
Winnipeg, MB R3C 1H3
Phone: (204) 957-3853
Fax: (204) 957-3792
Contact: W.H. Loewen, Director, or Lisa Shaw, Researcher

DESCRIPTION

Alone among the business groups appearing in this directory, this organization opposes free trade as envisioned by the three North American administrations. The council was formed in 1987 by 30 small- and medium-size businesses in a largely unsuccessful effort to counter the public image of businesses as unanimously in favor of the U.S.-Canada Free Trade Agreement.

ACTIVITIES

The council has shifted from its initial focus on political activity to providing research services.

RESOURCES

- With the exception of five issues of a newsletter timed for Canada's national elections in 1988, the results of the group's research are published by others.

Business Council on National Issues (BCNI)*

Royal Bank Centre
90 Sparks St. #806
Ottawa, ON K1P 5B4
Phone: (613) 238-3727
Fax: (613) 236-8679
Contact: Heidi Hutchings, Communications Assistant

DESCRIPTION

Patterned after the U.S. Business Roundtable, the BCNI is an influential research and lobbying organization whose members are the chief executive officers of 150 large Canadian corporations. Approximately one-third of these corporations are subsidiaries of U.S. multinationals. The council has a strong pro-free trade position, and is credited by some with converting Prime Minister Brian Mulroney to the free trader he is.

ACTIVITIES

The BCNI sponsors periodic forums, conducts research, and issues policy statements on a wide variety of national issues.

LINKS

The council enjoys close relations with many of Canada's government agencies in the current administration, and is active in a number of international organizations and global forums.

RESOURCES

- *National Economic Priorities: Challenges and Opportunities*. A perspective on the Canadian economy. Toronto, January 1991.
- *Canada-Mexico-United States Free Trade: A Canadian Business Perspective*. Submission to the House of Commons Standing Committee on External Affairs and International Trade. Ottawa, September 1990.
- *The Canada-United States Free Trade Agreement*, Submission to the Ontario Select Committee on Economic Affairs. Toronto, January 1988.
- *The Draft Canada-United States Free Trade Agreement*. Toronto, October 1987.

Canadian Chamber of Commerce*

55 Metcalfe St. #1160
Ottawa, ON K1P 6N4
Phone: (613) 238-4000
Fax: (613) 238-7643
Contact: Keith Martin, Director of International Policy

DESCRIPTION

The Canadian Chamber of Commerce is the nation's largest and most representative business association, comprising firms of every type and from every region of Canada. It proposes that any liberalization of trade between the United States and Mexico apply equally to Canada.

ACTIVITIES

The chamber monitors federal and international issues, solicits the views of the Canadian business community, and communicates them to policymakers in Ottawa. It provides leadership in anticipating major issues relating to economics, education, trade development, and international relations.

LINKS

In 1933, the Canadian and U.S. Chambers of Commerce founded the Committee on Canada-U.S. Relations to encourage communication between Canadian and U.S. businesspeople on bilateral policy issues. This committee monitors and evaluates public policy affecting trade and investment relations between the two countries, and recommends policy positions to the federal government in each nation.

Opened in January 1991, the chamber's unobtrusive office in Mexico City reflects the relatively small amount of Canadian investment in Mexico. Ten to 20 Canadian firms belong to the chamber, which has only one staff member. It is the only Canadian business group with operations in Mexico, and has worked closely with CEMAI during its brief existence. There is no Canadian Chamber of Commerce in the United States. The chamber's international operations are located at the main office.

OTHER OFFICES

Canadian Chamber of Commerce in Mexico
Rio de la Plata 30
Col. Cuauhtémoc
México, D.F.
Phone: (5) 2-86-25-26
Fax: (5) 2-86-25-26
Contact: Alicia Harsh, Secretary

Canadian Exporters' Association (CEA)*

99 rue Bank #250
Ottawa, ON K1P 6B9
Phone: (613) 238-8888 ext. 229
Fax: (613) 563-9218
Contact: James D. Moore, Vice-President for Policy

DESCRIPTION

The Canadian Exporters' Association is Canada's only national, nonprofit, and independent association concerned solely with supporting and increasing the potential of the Canadian exporting community.

ACTIVITIES

The group is involved in lobbying, consulting, and providing annual seminars for exporters, offering advice on exporting practices and techniques. It also advocates the interests of exporters before provincial and national governments, and international agencies.

LINKS

The CEA is in contact with the Department of External Affairs and International Trade; Department of Industry, Science and Technology; Department of Finance of Canada; Canadian International Development Agency; etc.

RESOURCES

- *Export News*. Bulletin. Information on Canadian export policies, tariff regulations and trade developments in other countries. It includes a special section devoted to U.S. trade, including legislation and regulatory changes affecting the U.S. market.
- *Export Digest*. A regular insert in *Export News* that surveys international trade publications and speeches from around the world. It includes a listing of current export opportunities.
- *Membership Directory*. Includes Canadian government contacts in Canada and abroad.
- A library with trade information: marketing, free trade zones, trade agreements, trade development policies, country reports, industrial linkages, and trade leads and referrals.

2. MEXICO

Consejo Empresarial Mexicano para Asuntos Internacionales (CEMAI)*

Homero 527, piso 7
México, D.F. 11570
Phone: (5) 2-50-70-33
Fax: (5) 5-31-13-90
Contact: Cecilia Laffán, North America section

DESCRIPTION

The Mexican Business Council for International Affairs (CEMAI) is the international arm of the Business Coordinating Council (CCE), Mexico's umbrella organization for the private sector. Its mission is to promote greater levels of trade, foreign investment, and international capital flows toward Mexico, and to establish and develop business relations with similar organizations worldwide. Toward this end, CEMAI operates a North America business section and maintains an office in Washington, DC, to monitor the impact of U.S. trade policy upon Mexico's international trade. It also coordinates 60 bilateral business committees in other countries co-chaired by a Mexican business leader and his/her foreign counterpart.

CEMAI'S Board of Trustees is composed of: the Business Coordinating Council (CCE), the Confederation of National Chambers of Commerce, Service and Tourism (CONCANACO), the Confederation of Industrial Chambers of the United States of Mexico (CONCAMIN), the Confederation of Employers of the Mexican Republic (COPARMEX), the Mexican Association of Insurance Institutions (AMIS), the National Chamber of Commerce of Mexico City (CANACO), the National Chamber of the Manufacturing Industry (CANACINTRA), the National Association of Stock Exchange Firms (AMCB), the National Agricultural and Livestock Council (CNA), and the Mexican Council of Businessmen (CMHN).

ACTIVITIES

CEMAI coordinates and supports the Mexican business community's participation in: bilateral business committees, bilateral or multilateral trade negotiations, international forums, foreign trade missions, and national and international trade fairs. It also lobbies before the Mexican and foreign governments on issues related to Mexico's international trade policy. CEMAI facilitates business communication and coordination with Mexico's Bank of External Trade (Bancomext) and its offices abroad, the diplomatic community in Mexico, and Mexican embassies abroad.

LINKS

Counterparts of CEMAI include the American Chamber of Commerce of Mexico, the Canadian Council of the Americas, and the U.S. Chamber of Commerce. Other international organizations with which CEMAI maintains close communication are the Conference Board of Canada, Conference Board of the U.S.A., and General Agreement on Tariffs and Trade (GATT).

RESOURCES

- Information concerning: Mexico's external trade, foreign investment, transfer of technology, foreign procurement opportunities and business deals, foreign trade barriers, and services and aid offered by the Mexican government regarding trade and investment issues.

Consejo Nacional de la Industria Maquiladora (CNIM)*

Ave. San Antonio #256, piso 4
Col. Ampliación Nápoles
México, D.F.
Phone: (5) 5-63-34-00 ext. 305
Fax: (5) 6-11-65-23
Contact: Alma Rosa Núñez Cáceres de Campos, Director

DESCRIPTION

Consejo Nacional de la Industria Maquiladora (the National Council of the Maquiladora Industry) is a binational business organization with a membership of 170 companies, most of them from the United States. The council compiles information about *maquiladoras*, makes proposals, and lobbies the Mexican government for greater benefits for its members. The CNIM operates branches in Ciudad Juárez, Tijuana, Chihuahua, Matamoros, Nogales, Reynosa, and Mexicali. Each branch is an independent regional association with close communication ties.

LINKS

The council has relations with the Border Trade Alliance.

OTHER OFFICES

Asociación de Maquiladoras de Ciudad Juárez
Río Nilo 4049 #10
Fraccionamiento Córdoba Américas
Ciudad Juárez, Chih. 32310
Phone: (16) 16-14-61
Fax: (16) 13-50-54
Contact: Cesar Alarcón, Director

Asociación de Maquiladoras de Tijuana
Blvd. Agua Caliente 10440 #6
Col. Revolución
Tijuana, B.C. 22400
Phone: (66) 86-14-87/88
Fax: (66) 86-15-11
Contact: Luis Alberto Pelayo

Coordinación de Organismos Empresariales de Comercio Exterior (COECE)*

Monte Cáucaso 915, piso 4
Col. Lomas de Chapultepec
México, D.F. 11000
Phone: (5) 2-59-03-14
Fax: (5) 5-40-15-52
Contact: Juan Gallardo Thurlow

DESCRIPTION

Formed in coordination with the government to define business' negotiating goals and strategies for the North American free trade talks, the Mexican Business Coordinating Council for NAFTA (COECE) enjoys unparalleled access to Mexico's negotiating team. "If they're not there sitting at the [negotiating] table, they're in the hallway," remarked one observer. Committees representing big businesses in all sectors of the economy develop reports and recommendations, which are then delivered to the government's negotiating team. COECE also has a Washington office (contact: Raul J. Ortega, managing director).

LINKS

COECE has links with the U.S. Coalition of Service Industries, the U.S. Industry Sector Advisory Committee on Service (ISAC-13), and the Canadian Association of Service industries.

Mexican Investment Board*

Paseo de la Reforma 915
Col. Lomas de Chapultepec
México, D.F. 11000
Phone: (5) 2-02-78-04
Fax: (5) 2-02-79-25
Contact: Aliza Chelminsky

DESCRIPTION

A joint venture between the Mexican government and a number of private financial institutions, the investment board is often the first place foreign investors go for information.

ACTIVITIES

Public relations and investor assistance dominate the board's activities. Through a New York public relations firm, the board has been able to place numerous articles and opinion pieces promoting Mexican investment opportunities in U.S. newspapers.

RESOURCES

- A series of profiles of Mexican industries and summaries of Mexican investment laws. Free from the New York office.

OTHER OFFICES

Mexican Investment Board
MIB New York
1500 Broadway #25
New York, NY 10036
Phone: (800) 642-2434
Fax: (212) 704-0129

3. UNITED STATES

American Chamber of Commerce of Mexico (AmCham)*

Lucerna 78
Col. Juárez
México, D.F. 06600
Phone: (5) 7-24-38-00
Fax: (5) 7-03-39-08
Contact: Mariana Prado, Director

DESCRIPTION

The American Chamber of Commerce (AmCham) is a nonprofit, self-financed association dedicated to promote trade and investment between Mexico and the United States. Since 1917, it has provided professional business services to U.S. companies interested in operating in Mexico. AmCham's commercial information is viewed as the most authoritative guide on establishing a *maquiladora* plant in Mexico.

RESOURCES

- Its commercial division supplies names and addresses of Mexican manufacturers, potential suppliers, importers, and exporters. Its economic and financial data aids in forecasting and planning.
- *Business Mexico*. Monthly statistical journal related to Mexico's economy, government policies, industry and labor affairs. Overviews of investment and trade prospects.
- *Membership Directory*. An annual commercial reference listing the field of activity, senior executives, addresses, phone, telex, and fax numbers of its 2,900 corporate members. Includes relevant economic information, forecasts of GNP by sector, projections of public finances, and data about American Chambers of Commerce overseas. Bilingual index. 372 pages. Free for members.
- *Directory of American Companies*. Details from over 3,000 firms operating in Mexico. Bilingual. 650 pages.
- *Data Bank Diskettes*. Includes the most important economic indicators in Mexico and in other countries, as well as the AmCham forecast for the Mexican and American economies. Provides historical economic data (1978-90), and reports on the external, production, labor, financial, and monetary sectors. Bilingual. Available in computer disk format, three 5 1/4-inch diskettes.
- *Encuesta de Prestaciones*. Information about the benefits offered in Mexico to personnel at the executive level and to trusted employees. The *Encuesta* is arranged by size, location, and kind of business. Spanish. 49 pages.
- *COMEXUS*. A monthly information bulletin about international commerce and U.S.-Mexico commercial relations. Spanish.
- *Survey of Salaries*. A guide containing current information on executive-level and salaried employee positions. Arranged by company size, location, and industrial sector, this study supplies data on average base pay, total monthly guaranteed compensation, and personnel costs to the company. Bilingual. 630 pages.
- *Maquiladora Handbook*. Up-to-date *maquiladora* developments. English. 315 pages.
- Other publications include the *Manual para el Importador Mexicano*, and the *Manual para el Exportador Mexicano*.

Border Trade Alliance (BTA)*

PO Box 2682
Laredo, TX 78044-2682
Phone: (800) 282-6311
Fax: (210) 722-6247
Contact: Angela Shipton

DESCRIPTION

The Border Trade Alliance (BTA) is a grassroots alliance of U.S.-Mexico border organizations. It acts as a forum for its participants to discuss and advocate the interests of the border. Operating as a network of economic development corporations, chambers of commerce, trade associations, banks, industrial parks, service providers, manufacturers, and state and local government agencies, it works to educate, build consensus, and solve problems. Its policy objectives include promotion of transborder commerce between the United States and Mexico, the development of necessary resources for border economic growth, and the advocacy of private- and public-sector border interests in the regulatory and legislative process. BTA issues of concern are: U.S./Mexico trade; customs policies, procedures and facilities; in-bond industry; transportation; and health and the environment.

ACTIVITIES

BTA is active in organizing conferences in Mexico and the United States.

Business Roundtable*

1615 L St. NW
Washington, DC 20036
Phone: (202) 872-1260
Fax: (202) 466-3509
Contacts: Pat Engman, Executive Director

DESCRIPTION

An association of 200 corporate chief executive officers (CEOs), the Roundtable seeks to establish and publicize a business perspective on national economic issues. The chairperson of the Task Force on International Trade and Investment, American Express CEO James Robinson III, is a vigorous and high-profile supporter of NAFTA.

ACTIVITIES

Research, government relations, and public information dominate the Roundtable's agenda. Position papers are distributed to members of Congress and are often cited in the press.

RESOURCES

- *Building a Comprehensive U.S.-Mexico Economic Relationship: Preliminary Negotiating Objectives of The Business Roundtable*. June 1991.

Chambers of Commerce

Of the hundreds of chambers of commerce in the United States, we have selected the following list, composed of those whose bi/trinational activities most frequently and directly deal with free trade negotiations.

Brownsville Chamber of Commerce
1600 E. Elizabeth St.
PO Box 752
Brownsville, TX 78522-0752
Phone: (512) 542-4341

California Hispanic Chamber of Commerce
PO Box 77346
San Francisco, CA 94107
Phone: (415) 905-6869
Contact: Manuel A. Rosales, President

Chicago Association of Commerce & Industry
200 N. LaSalle St.
Chicago, IL 60601
Phone: (312) 580-6900
Fax: (312) 580-0046
Contact: Robert Lahey, Director of World Trade

El Paso Chamber of Commerce
10 Civic Center Plaza
El Paso, TX 79987
Phone: (915) 534-0500
Fax: (915) 534-0513
Contact: Burt Diamondstein, Vice-President, Industrial Development

El Paso Hispanic Chamber of Commerce
PO Box 26832
El Paso, TX 79926
Phone: (915) 566-4066
Contact: Charles Ponzio, Jr., President

Greater Detroit Chamber of Commerce
600 W. Lafayette Blvd.
Detroit, MI 48226
Phone: (313) 964-4000
Fax: (313) 964-0531
Contact: Ernest Olsen, Manager Export Business

Greater San Diego Chamber of Commerce
402 W. Broadway #1000
San Diego, CA 92101-3585
Phone: (619) 232-0124
Fax: (619) 234-0571
Contact: Bernice Layton, VP for International Affairs

Illinois State Chamber of Commerce
20 N. Wacker Drive
Chicago, IL 60606-3083
Phone: (312) 372-7373

Laredo Chamber of Commerce
PO Box 790
Laredo, TX 78040-0790
Phone: (210) 722-9895
Fax: (210) 722-5528
Contact: Cathy García, Director

Los Angeles Area Chamber of Commerce
404 S. Bixel St.
PO Box 3696
Los Angeles, CA 90051-1696
Phone: (213) 629-0602
Fax: (213) 629-0708
Contact: Corinne Muratt, International Manager

Texas State Chamber of Commerce
300 W. 15th St. #875
Austin, TX 78701
Phone: (512) 472-1594
Fax: (512) 320-0280

Council of Great Lakes Governors

Canadian Trade Liaison Office
121 Richmond St. W. #121
Toronto, ON M5H 2K1
Phone: (416) 368-6956
Fax: (416) 368-2547

DESCRIPTION

The Council of Great Lakes Governors, a private, nonprofit organization established in 1983, has established a Canadian Trade Liaison office in Canada on behalf of its eight member states: Illinois, Indiana, Michigan, Minnesota, New York, Ohio, Pennsylvania, and Wisconsin.

ACTIVITIES

The office supplements the existing trade-promotion activities of its member states, assisting companies with information on market prospects and distribution channels. It also represents firms from the region at trade shows in target sectors.

Enterprise of the Americas Program*

North-South Center
PO Box 248123
Coral Gables, FL 33124-3010
Phone: (305) 284-4414
Fax: (305) 284-5089
Contact: Peter B. Field, Director

DESCRIPTION

The Enterprise of the Americas Program assists small- and medium-size firms in Canada, the Caribbean, Latin America, and the United States in gaining maximum practical benefits from the move toward a hemispheric free trade zone. Priority is given to establishing consortium activities and linkages with universities and research institutions in the hemisphere, enabling further investigation and promotion of the process of trade and investment liberalization. The program provides a forum for Latin American and Caribbean entrepreneurs to explore with their North American counterparts potential "winners and losers" as the free trade process moves forward. The group supports the U.S. government's Enterprise for the Americas Initiative (EAI).

ACTIVITIES

Through forums, symposiums, and workshops, the program helps small-business leaders learn from each other and from public-policy leaders how to influence domestic structural reforms in their own countries and how to help shape the ongoing subregional economic-integration process. These activities are augmented by an outreach program to business associations in the hemisphere aimed at strengthening public awareness and interest.

Mexican Chamber of Commerce of Arizona*

PO Box 626
Phoenix, AZ 85001
Phone: (602) 252-6448
Contact: Hector E. Ledesma, President

DESCRIPTION

The primary function of this chamber of commerce is to assist U.S. firms who want to do business in Mexico by arranging corporate contacts and face-to-face meetings with Mexican businesspeople. It has a branch in Hermosillo, Sonora.

Mexico-U.S. Business Committee*

U.S. Section
c/o Council of the Americas
1625 K St. NW #1200
Washington, DC 20006
Phone: (202) 659-1547
Fax: (202) 659-0169
Contact: Colleen S. Morton, Director

DESCRIPTION

The committee describes itself as the oldest private-sector organization linking the United States and Mexico. Its corporate members—57 on the U.S. side alone—are the elite of the business class in each country. Membership in the committee provides executives the opportunity to establish cross-border relationships with their foreign counterparts and with high-level government officials. The committee is essentially an arm of the Council of the Americas, headed by David Rockefeller, but is co-sponsored by the American Chamber of Commerce in Mexico and the Chamber of Commerce of the United States.

ACTIVITIES

Consistent with its primary function—networking—the committee frequently hosts high-level government officials from the United States and Mexico. Many events are open to the public, but most valuable to corporate members are the small, private sessions which, as the council's brochure indicates, "assist in problem-solving by providing access to Latin American and U.S.-government officials for discussion of company-specific issues."

RESOURCES

- *Washington Report*. Published by the Council of the Americas ten times per year. $200/yr. for nonmembers.

U.S. Hispanic Chamber of Commerce (USHCC)*

2000 M St. NW #860
Washington, DC 20009
Phone: (202) 862-3939
Fax: (202) 862-3947
Contact: Miguel Díaz

DESCRIPTION

The U.S. Hispanic Chamber of Commerce (USHCC) promotes Hispanic-owned business both with corporate America and with agencies of the federal government. At the international level, the chamber is involved in the NAFTA negotiations.

ACTIVITIES

Through the USHCC's headquarters in Washington, and through its western regional office in Los Angeles, the chamber offers a business development service that allocates resources to facilitate the participation of Hispanic enterprises in the mainstream of the U.S. economy. The chamber also encourages the involvement of Hispanic-owned businesses in NAFTA negotiations and urges their endorsement of a future economically integrated hemispheric bloc.

RESOURCES

- *Legislative Update*. Monthly. Highlights USHCC legislative and regulatory initiatives and accomplishments. $150/yr. for nonmembers in the U.S., $155/yr. in Mexico and Canada, $170/yr. in other countries.
- *Networking*. Official quarterly newsletter of the USHCC.
- *Convention Magazine*. Published once a year. $100/yr. Free for members.

U.S.-Mexico Chamber of Commerce

1211 Connecticut Ave. NW #510
Washington, DC 20036
Phone: (202) 296-5198
Fax: (202) 822-0075
Contact: Martin Rojas

DESCRIPTION

As with other chambers, the U.S.-Mexico Chamber of Commerce provides research services to its members, including information about markets, quotas, tariffs, and potential cross-border partners for business ventures. The chamber is also able to provide some information to the public. There are branch offices in Los Angeles, Dallas, and New York, and a representative office located at CEMAI in Mexico City.

Western Maquiladora Trade Association (WMTA)*

PO Box 3746
Chula Vista, CA 91909-0255
Phone: (619) 420-9682
Fax: (619) 575-5792
Contact: Alfred Rich, President

DESCRIPTION

Boasting 200 member companies—a majority of U.S. companies on both sides of the border, WMTA supports the fast-track process for NAFTA.

ACTIVITIES

The association concentrates on long-range, strategy-oriented issues such as how to improve the business environment. One of its present activities is a directory of suppliers and other support industries in the Tijuana/San Diego region.

LINKS

Collaborates with the Border Trade Alliance.

PART VIII

Electronic Networking

INTRODUCTION

The global emergence of electronic communication networks is making it possible for local organizations to coordinate and communicate with their counterparts all over the world. The inclusion of an email (electronic mail) address for so many of the organizations listed in this directory is evidence of the growing importance of electronic networking in bi/trinational relations. Electronic networking allows users to send a letter, bulletin or message to one or several contacts in a matter of seconds, to participate in discussions within international social movements, and to maintain contact with key members of an organization or network, all from a personal computer. These networks also provide access to alternative news services around the world. All that is needed is a personal computer (IBM- or Macintosh-compatible), a modem, a telephone line, and membership in an electronic network. Although several networks are available, the following list includes some of the networks most popular with organizations listed in this directory.

One particularly helpful resource for electronic networking is *North American NGO Computer Networking Against NAFTA: The Use of Computer Communications in Cross-Border Coalition Building*, by Howard H. Frederick, September 1992. This report summarizes the role that global communication technology is playing within the nongovernmental community. The paper also describes the emergence of the Association for Progressive Communication (APC), a global information and communication computer network, and examines trilateral networking efforts. Most useful is a comprehensive list of email addresses for nongovernmental organizations working on U.S.-Mexican relations. This report is available from the Department of Politics and Society, University of California, Irvine, PO Box 94653, Pasadena, CA 91109. Phone: (818) 568-0994. Fax: (818) 791-2205, "Attention CLAIRE". Email: hfrederick@igc.apc.org. Contact: Howard H. Frederick.

Institute for Global Communications (IGC)*
PeaceNet, EcoNet, Telepac

18 De Boom St.
San Francisco, CA 94107
Phone: (415) 442-0220
Fax: (415) 546-1794
Email: igc:support

DESCRIPTION

Offered by the Institute for Global Communications to U.S. subscribers are PeaceNet and EcoNet. IGC is also currently planning a regional network for Mexican members. To subscribe to any of IGC's networks send your name, address, phone number, suggested electronic address, and some key words describing your interest and work, as well as a credit card number or $50 deposit.

PeaceNet interconnects members in the United States and Mexico with international email, conferences, and user directories. EcoNet is devoted to helping the environmental movement throughout the world to communicate and cooperate more effectively and efficiently. It links activists throughout the United States and 70 different countries, allowing them to create global alliances. PeaceNet and EcoNet cost: $10 sign-up fee and $10 per month membership fee. Every additional peak hour is $10, and every additional off-peak hour is $5.

RESOURCES

Labor Coalition for Communications about NAFTA

Description

Forged by participants at the Labor Tech Conference in December 1992, this computer link aims to improve electronic communications among activists from the United States, Mexico and Canada. The Labor Coalition's information exchange goes through web.freetrade on APC (PeaceNet in the United States and WEB in Canada) and "freetrade" on Solinet.

Immigration and Border Issues: Cross-Border Networks and Coalitions
Email: pol.immigrante
Contact: Armando Martínez, Center for U.S.-Mexican Studies

OTHER OFFICES

Telepac
Eje Central Lázaro Cárdenas 567
Col. Narvarte
México, D.F. 03020
Phone: (5) 5-30-20-99

Description

Telepac is an electronics communications network that allows visitors to Mexico access to IGC networks at discounted rates. Users of Telepac must have existing personal or institutional accounts with IGC, and they must arrange payment of a $25 one-time membership fee to the Mexican cooperative. A monthly surcharge of $3 covers one hour of access from Mexico; additional access time is $3 per hour, prorated by minutes. Interested users should contact dbarkin, mam, or sipro for further information.

SoliNet

21 Florence St.
Ottawa, ON K2P 0W6
Phone: (613) 594-5113

DESCRIPTION

SoliNet is an electronic network dealing with labor issues in Canada. The network, founded in the early 1980s, has about 700 active users. It hosts a number of computer conferences on health, safety, women, and labor. SoliNet offers on-line databases on collective bargaining, grievances, and contacts. It is used by unions to coordinate collective bargaining and lobbying efforts as well as to share information on health and safety.

WEB

c/o NIRV
456 Spadina Ave. #2
Toronto, ON M5T 2G8
Phone: (416) 596-0212
Fax: (416) 974-9189

DESCRIPTION

WEB is a network of Canadian organizations and individuals that can now be connected to their U.S. counterparts through PeaceNet. Members of WEB have access to international email, user directories, and conferences. Cost: Same as PeaceNet. WEB is affiliated with IGC.

APPENDIX

1. When calling long distance:

TO CALL OR FAX FROM MEXICO TO:

Canada or United States: 95 INTERNATIONAL LONG DISTANCE + (CITY AREA CODE) + LOCAL NUMBER

= 95 (505) 842-8288

TO CALL OR FAX FROM THE UNITED STATES OR CANADA TO:

Mexico: 011 + (COUNTRY NUMBER) + (CITY AREA CODE) + LOCAL NUMBER

= 011 (52) (5) 5-39-00-15

Canada: 1 + (CITY AREA CODE) + LOCAL NUMBER

2. Note about the addresses:

- a # after the name of the street means: suite, apartment, floor, room, despacho. It does not mean the number of the building in the street. In the U.S. and Canadian addresses, building numbers always appear at the beginning of the line. In Mexican addresses, the building number appears after the street name.
- Phone or fax numbers containing a / indicate multiple phone numbers. For example:

  (5) 5-39-00-15/55 means

  (5) 5-39-00-15 or (5) 5-39-00-55
- Col. = Colonia (Neighborhood)
- Edif. = Edificio (Building)
- A.P. = Apartado Postal (PO Box)

3. Abbreviations of Canadian provinces:

AB = Alberta

BC = British Columbia

MB = Manitoba

NB = New Brunswick

NF = Newfoundland

NS = Nova Scotia

ON = Ontario

PE = Prince Edward Island

PQ = Québec

SK = Saskatchewan

4. Abbreviations of Mexican states:

Ags. = Aguascalientes

B.C. = Baja California

B.C.S. = Baja California Sur

Cam. = Campeche

Chis. = Chiapas

Chih. = Chihuahua

Coah. = Coahuila
Col. = Colima
Dgo. = Durango
Edo. de Mex. = Estado de México
Gto. = Guanajuato
Gro. = Guerrero
Hgo. = Hidalgo
Jal. = Jalisco
D.F. = Distrito Federal = Mexico City
Mich. = Michoacán
Mor. = Morelos
Nay. = Nayarit
N.L. = Nuevo León
Oax. = Oaxaca
Pue. = Puebla
Qro. = Querétaro
Q. Roo = Quintana Roo
S.L.P. = San Luis Potosí
Sin. = Sinaloa
Son. = Sonora
Tab. = Tabasco
Tamps. = Tamaulipas
Tlax. = Tlaxcala
Ver. = Veracrúz
Yuc. = Yucatán
Zac. = Zacatecas

5. Abbreviations of U.S. states:

AL = Alabama
AK = Alaska
AZ = Arizona
AR = Arkansas
CA = California
CO = Colorado
CT = Connecticut
DE = Delaware
DC = District of Columbia
FL = Florida
GA = Georgia
GU = Guam
HI = Hawaii
ID = Idaho
IL = Illinois
IN = Indiana
IA = Iowa
KS = Kansas
KY = Kentucky
LA = Louisiana
ME = Maine
MD = Maryland
MA = Massachusetts
MI = Michigan
MN = Minnesota
MS = Mississippi
MO = Missouri
MT = Montana
NE = Nebraska
NV = Nevada
NH = New Hampshire
NJ = New Jersey
NM = New Mexico
NY = New York
NC = North Carolina
ND = North Dakota
OH = Ohio
OK = Oklahoma
OR = Oregon
PA = Pennsylvania
PR = Puerto Rico
RI = Rhode Island
SC = South Carolina
SD = South Dakota
TN = Tennessee
TX = Texas
UT = Utah
VT = Vermont
VA = Virginia
VI = Virgin Islands
WA = Washington
WV = West Virginia
WI = Wisconsin
WY = Wyoming

INDEX

A

B

C

D

E

F

G

H

I

M

N

O

P

R

S

T

U

W

Y

ADDENDUM

The first edition of *Cross-Border Links* sold out in less than a year, and this reprinting has given us an opportunity to make a limited number of corrections, additions, and updates (a completely updated and revised edition of *Cross-Border Links* will be published in late 1994). We are gratified that the first printing of *Cross-Border Links* sold so quickly—a possible indication of the widespread desire to create citizen links across national borders.

This addendum attempts to deal with major changes that could not be easily included in the main text. The following list includes new organizations or ones that were missed in the first edition. In the case of SEDUE/SEDESOL, the entry concerns the complete reorganization of this government agency. Two institutions included in the directory have shut their doors since the first printing of *Cross-Border Links*: Foro Mexicano de la Sociedad Civil/Rio 92 (page 72), and the San Diego Mayor's Office of Binational Affairs (page 205). Two networking organizations, Citizen Trade Watch Campaign and Fair Trade Campaign, joined together to form one umbrella organization: the Citizens' Trade Campaign (CTC). In addition, two organizations have changed their names: the U.S.-Mexico-Canada Labor Solidarity Network changed its name to North American Worker-to-Worker Network (NAWWN), and Mobilization on Development, Trade, Labor and the Environment (MODTLE) changed its name to Alliance for Responsible Trade (ART). We encourage organizations to complete the questionnaire that follows and to send us additions or corrections for the next edition of the directory. Please include the *Cross-Border Links* project of the Resource Center on your mailing list so that we are aware of your activities and publications.

The following listing is organized the same as the original text of *Cross-Border Links*, first by category, and then by country.

PART I / Networks for Fair Trade

3. UNITED STATES

Alliance for Responsible Trade (ART)
PO Box 74
100 Maryland Ave NE
Washington, D.C. 20002
Phone: (202) 544-7198 Fax: (202) 543-5999
Contact: Pharis Harvey, Coordinator

Citizens' Trade Campaign (CTC)
215 Pennsylvania Ave SE
Washington, D.C. 20003
Phone: (202) 554-1102 Fax: (202) 554-1654
Contact: Jim Jontz or Scott Paul

North American Worker-to-Worker Network (NAWWN)
PO Box 6003
Durham, NC 27708-6003
Phone/fax: (919) 286-5617
Contact: Jacki Van Anda

PART II / Labor

2. MEXICO

Comité Fronterizo de Obreras (CFO)
Matamoros, Tamps.
Phone: (891) 7-26-33/7-56/14
U.S. address: PO Box 1206, Edinburg, TX 78540
Contact: María Guadalupe Torres Martínez

PART III / Environment

2. MEXICO

Bioconservación
A.P. 504
San Nicolás de la Garza, N.L. 66450
Phone: (83) 76-22-31
Contact: Salvador Contreras Balderas

Comité Cívico de Divulgación Ecológica (CCDEAC)
Madero 1117, Col. Nueva
Mexicali, B.C.
Phone: (65) 52-20-80 Fax: (65) 52-98-12
U.S. mailing address: PO Box 1094, Calexico, CA 92231
Contact: Fernando Medina Robles

Red Fronteriza de Salud y Ambiente
c/o El Colegio de Sonora
Av. Obregón 54
Hermosillo, Son. 83000
Phone: (62) 12-65-51/50-21
Contact: Catalina Denman

3. UNITED STATES

Binational Health and Environment Coalition of Ambos Nogales
c/o Rural Health Office
University of Arizona
2501 E. Elm Street
Tucson, AZ 85716
Phone: (602) 626-7946 Fax: (602) 326-6429
Contact: Jill Guernsey de Zapien

Binational Network
c/o Texas Center for Policy Studies
PO Box 2618
Austin, TX 78768
Phone: (512) 474-0811 Fax: (512) 478-8140
Contact: Mary Kelly

Comité Consenso Internacional
6842 Tanque Verde Road #D
Tucson, AZ 85715
Phone: (602) 290-0828 Fax: (602) 290-0969
Contact: Wendy Laird

International Youth Alliance
Audubon Society (Brownsville-Matamoros)
PO Box 5052
Brownsville, TX 78523
Phone: (210) 541-8034 Fax: (210) 546-4446
Contact: Karen Chapman or Rose Farmer

Pacific Industry Health, Inc. (Pacific IHI)
2830 10th Street
Berkeley, CA 94710
Phone: (510) 845-3146 Fax: (510) 845-4015
Contact: Garrett Brown

Project del Rio
PO Box 30001, Department 3R
New Mexico State University
Las Cruces, NM 88003-0001
Phone: (505) 646-5745
Contact: Lisa LaRocque, Director
Contact in Ciudad Juárez: Patricia Martínez Tellez
Phone: (16) 166-6606 (ext. 3856)

San Luis R.C., Sonora/Yuma County, Arizona, Binational Health and Environment Council
281 W. 24th Street #120
Yuma, AZ 85364
Phone: (602) 726-8270 Fax: (602) 344-4731
Contact: Amanda Aguirre

PART IV / Advocacy Organizations

3. UNITED STATES

BorderLinks
924 N. 6th Ave.
Tucson, AZ 85705
Phone: (602) 628-8263
Email: (PeaceNet) borderlinks
Contact: Cristina Graber

Global Exchange
2017 Mission Street #303
San Francisco, CA 94110
Phone: (415) 255-7296 Fax: (415) 255-7498
Contact: Rose Williams

Mexico Information Project
8124 W. Third Street #212
Los Angeles, CA 90048
Phone: (213) 852-0778
Contact: Teresa Sanchez

NAFTA/GATT Justice Committee
PO Box 10023
Olympia, WA 98502
Phone: (206) 786-8950
Contact: Kelly James

North American Institute
128 Grand Ave #106
Santa Fe, NM 87501
Phone: (505) 982-3657 Fax: (505) 983-5840
Contact: John Wirth or Kathleen Lyons

Rio Grande Border Witness Program
PO Box 3382
Harlingen, TX 78551
Phone: (210) 428-8418
Contact: Sister M. Ellen Lamberjack

PART VI / Government Agencies

2. MEXICO

SECRETARIA DE DESARROLLO SOCIAL (SEDESOL)

Instituto Nacional de Ecología (INE)
Río Elba 20 1er. piso, Col. Cuauhtemoc
México, D.F. 06500
Phone: (5) 5-53-95-38/94-81/29-77 Fax: (5) 2-86-85-59
Contact: Sergio Reyes Luján, President, or René Altamirano

Procuraduría Federal de Protección al Medio Ambiente
Boulevar Pípila 1
Tecamachalco, Naucalpan de Juárez
Edo. de México 53950
Phone: (5) 5-89-89-83/01-66 or 6-89-43-45 Fax: (5) 589-74-83
Contact: Santiago Oñate Laborde, Procurador General

Description

SEDESOL's main functions are environmental policy formulation and enforcement, urban planning, and administration of the National Solidarity Program (PRONASOL). SEDESOL's environmental functions are divided between two autonomous agencies: the Instituto Nacional de Ecología/INE (National Institute of Ecology) and Procuraduría

Federal de Protección al Medio Ambiente (The Attorney General for Protection of the Environment)

The Institute is responsible for research, formulation and evaluation of Mexico's environmental protection policies, and the implementation of environmental protection programs. The Office of the Attorney General enforces environmental regulations formulated by the National Institute of Ecology, investigates and penalizes non-compliance with environmental regulations, and provides direct access for and responses to public complaints regarding environmental non-compliance and activities harmful to the environment.

Other Offices

Dirección General de Ecología del Estado de Baja California
PO Box 432434
San Ysidro, CA 92143
Phone: (66) 84-05-35 Fax: (66) 84-03-72
Contact: Jorge Barroso

Procuraduría Federal de Protección al Medio Ambiente
Revolución III, Col. Centro
Hermosillo, Son. 83260
Phone/fax: (62) 13-28-38
Contact: Patricia Celis

Procuraduría Federal de Protección al Medio Ambiente-Cd. Juárez
Parque Chamizal s/n
A.P. 965
Ciudad Juárez, Chih.
Phone: (16) 13-76-38
Contact: Alfonso J. Amaral

Procuraduría Federal de Protección al Medio Ambiente-Mexicali
Palacio Federal, nivel 2, cuerpo "A"
Centro Cívico Comercial
Mexicali, B.C. 21000
Phone: (65) 56-07-01
Contact: Luis López Moctezuma, Delegado Estatal

Secretaría de Infraestructura Urbana y Ecología (SIUE)
Secretaría de Ecología del Estado de Sonora
Palacio Administrativo
Hermosillo, Son.
Phone: (62) 17-26-53/25 or 13-19-66 Fax: (62) 13-19-00
Contact: Ignacio Cabrera Fernández

UPDATE INFORMATION

for the second edition of **Cross-Border Links**

Please print or type. Attach an additional page if needed.

☐ You are a representative of the organization for which you are sending information.

☐ You are not a representative of the organization for which you are sending information.

Full name of the organization:

____

Recognized acronym: ______________________________

Former name (if any): ______________________________

☐ Main office ☐ Branch office ☐ Local office

Address: ______________________________

____

____

Telephone number: ______________________________

Fax number: ______________________________

Email (network with which you are connected: PeaceNet, EcoNet, etc, with address):

____

Contact(s): ______________________________

Name and description of your organization's projects specifically related to relations between the United States, Mexico, and Canada. Explain with all necessary details. If you are enclosing brochures or other materials, please mark the most important facts and the updated information.

____

____

____

____

In which section of the directory do you suggest your organization be included?

☐ Fair Trade Networks ☐ Labor ☐ Environment ☐ Advocacy Organizations
☐ Academic Institutions ☐ Government Agencies ☐ Business Groups
☐ Electronic Networks ☐ Other new section: ______________________________